Picture Processing
by Computer

Computer Science and Applied Mathematics

A SERIES OF MONOGRAPHS AND TEXTBOOKS

Edited by
Werner Rheinboldt
University of Maryland

Hans P. Künzi, H. G. Tzschach, and C. A. Zehnder
NUMERICAL METHODS OF MATHEMATICAL OPTIMIZATION: WITH ALGOL
AND FORTRAN PROGRAMS, 1968

Azriel Rosenfeld
PICTURE PROCESSING BY COMPUTER, 1969

Picture Processing
by Computer

AZRIEL ROSENFELD

Computer Science Center
University of Maryland
College Park, Maryland

ACADEMIC PRESS   New York   London   1969

ACADEMIC PRESS, INC.
111 Fifth Avenue, New York, New York 10003

United Kingdom Edition published by
ACADEMIC PRESS, INC. (LONDON) LTD.
Berkeley Square House, London W1X6BA

LIBRARY OF CONGRESS CATALOG CARD NUMBER: 78-84255

Second Printing, 1971

PRINTED IN THE UNITED STATES OF AMERICA

To My Wife

Contents

Over the past fifteen years, much effort has been devoted to developing methods of processing pictorial information by computer. This work has had a number of different goals, among them television bandwidth compression, image "enhancement" and "restoration," and pictorial pattern recognition. Most of the research in the field of picture processing has been directed toward the solution of specific problems, usually involving particular classes of pictures; but a body of "general-purpose" picture processing techniques is gradually being built up. This book treats the subject of picture processing from a primarily technique-oriented, rather than problem-oriented, standpoint.

We shall consider in this book only the processing of *given* pictures, not of pictures that have been synthesized by computer; this restriction rules out the areas of computer graphics, computer-generated movies, computer typography, and the like. As a further restriction, we shall be concerned only with pictures as *two*-*dimensional* objects; this excludes pictorial representations of three spatial dimensions (stereopairs, contour maps, the "hidden line problem," etc.) as well as time-varying pictorial information (e.g., on-line character recognition in real time). We shall not discuss techniques for computer input or output of pictures; on this subject see, e.g., A. van Dam, Computer driven displays and their use in man/machine interaction, *Advances Comput.* **7**, 239–290, 1966.

The concepts and techniques of picture processing have arisen from many different disciplines, among them mathematics, computer science, electrical engineering, and optics. In consequence, the topics treated in this book have a wide variety of prerequisites. For much of the book, a good background in calculus is required. Beyond this level, an attempt has been made to make the book relatively self-contained by reviewing the needed background material at the beginning of each section. Occasional "asides," not essential to the main development, that require concepts beyond the level of the rest of the book have been indented to set them off from the body of the text. Exercises that are relatively difficult, or that require special knowledge for their solution, have been starred.

References to the published literature (and in a very few cases, to the report literature) are given at the end of each section. Some general references to major collections of papers (for the most part, proceedings of meetings), which will be cited repeatedly, are given in the last section of Chapter 1.

The help of the following individuals in providing material for the figures is gratefully acknowledged: Dr. J. L. Harris (Figure 6.6), Mr. F. Rotz (Figures 5.10 and 6.4), and Mr. J. Strong (Figures 5.7, 5.8, and 6.5). Figures 3.1, 6.1–6.3, 6.7–6.11, 6.14, 8.1, 8.2, and 8.6 were produced at the University of Maryland by Edgar Butt, Yung H. Lee, and Andrew Pilipchuk.

Much of the subject matter of this book was presented by the author (in collaboration with a number of guest lecturers) in a short course on pictorial data processing given at Yeshiva University in August 1963, and in a short course on image processing given at the University of Maryland in June 1965. A draft of the book served as lecture notes in a graduate course on computer processing of pictorial information at the University of Maryland during the fall semester of 1967–1968. It is a pleasure to acknowledge the support of the Office of Naval Research, Information Systems Branch, under Contract Nonr-5144(00), which helped to make possible the preparation of these notes.

Credit is due to the many students whose attendance at these courses provided an opportunity to test preliminary versions of the book. "I have learned much from my teachers; still more, from my colleagues; and most of all, from my pupils."

AZRIEL ROSENFELD

June 1969

CHAPTER 1

Pictures and Picture Processing

In this chapter we define a "picture" or "picture function" as a mathematical object and justify the use of mathematical operations on pictures, as described in later chapters, by showing that picture functions are "indistinguishable from" functions that are well-behaved in various senses. We also briefly survey the types of picture processing problems that will be considered in the remainder of the book.

1.1. Picture Functions

The term "picture" suggests a flat object whose appearance varies from point to point. In a "black-and-white" picture this variation can be described by a single parameter, corresponding to the total amount of light reaching the observer from the given point; in colored pictures several parameters are required. Since picture processing research has dealt almost exclusively with black-and-white pictures, we shall assume from now on that only a single parameter is involved.

In accordance with the above remarks, we can formally define a *picture* (or more fully, to avoid confusion, a *picture function*) to be a real-valued function of two real variables. Since a physical picture is of finite extent, we can suppose that the function is nonzero only in a bounded region, which we can assume, without loss of generality, to be of some standard size and shape, e.g., square. In fact it is reasonable to assume that there is an upper bound to the possible size of any physical picture, so that we can suppose that any picture function is zero outside a square of prespecified size.

The value of a picture function at a point will be called the *gray level* of the picture at that point. Since the amount of light reaching the observer from a physical picture is finite and nonnegative, we can assume that any picture function is bounded and nonnegative. In fact here again it is reasonable to suppose that there is an upper bound M to the possible brightness of any physical picture, so that, for any picture function f, we have $0 \leq f(x, y) \leq M$ for all (x, y).

In processing pictures we shall sometimes want to perform a mathematical operation on a picture function—e.g., take its Fourier transform. In order to guarantee that such operations can actually be performed, it is necessary to assume that the picture function is in some sense analytically well-behaved, e.g., integrable, continuous, etc. We shall show at the end of this section that such assumptions are justified in the sense that any picture function is "indistinguishable from" an analytically well-behaved function.

When we process pictures by digital computer, we usually want to regard them as discrete arrays of numbers, i.e., as matrices, rather than as functions. Indeed, any matrix (having real, nonnegative elements) can be thought of as defining a "piecewise constant" picture function. For example, for each (i, j), where $1 \leq i \leq n$ and $1 \leq j \leq n$, let S_{ij} be the square defined by $i - 1 \leq x < i$ and $j - 1 \leq y < j$; then, to any n-by-n matrix (a_{ij}), we can associate the picture function that takes on the constant value a_{ij} on the square S_{ij}, for each (i, j). Such a picture function will be called a *digital picture function*.† [We shall often speak of the matrix (a_{ij}) as being (rather than merely defining) a digital picture.] It is easily shown (see below) that any picture function is indistinguishable from an n-by-n digital picture function for sufficiently large values of n.

It is also often desirable, particularly in digital picture processing, to assume that a picture function can take on only a finite set of values—in other words, that its gray levels are *quantized*. Here again, it is easy to show that any picture function is indistinguishable from a quantized picture function, provided that sufficiently many levels are allowed. An important special case is that of a *binary-valued* picture function, which can take on only two values ("black" and "white"—no intermediate gray levels), usually 0 and 1.

In the following paragraphs we justify, or at least rationalize, the statements made about arbitrary picture functions being indistinguishable from functions of various special types. Let $\mathscr{S}$ be a set of functions. We shall say that the function f is indistinguishable from a function in the set $\mathscr{S}$ if, for any $\delta > 0$ and any $\varepsilon > 0$, there exists a g

† The choice of coordinates in this example is meant for illustrative purposes only; such a piecewise constant picture function in any position, or at any scale, would also be called a digital picture function.

in $\mathscr{S}$ such that $|f(x, y) - g(x, y)| < \varepsilon$ for all (x, y) except those in a set of measure less than δ.

Now it is reasonable to assume that any picture function is integrable, since physically the integration corresponds to measuring the total amount of light reaching the observer from the picture. Let A be a square outside and on the border of which we have $f = 0$. Since f is integrable on A, for any $\delta > 0$ and $\varepsilon > 0$, there exists a function g, absolutely continuous on A, such that $|f - g| < \varepsilon$ except on a set of measure $< \delta$; and readily we can define $g = 0$ outside A without changing this situation. (See, e.g., E. C. Titchmarsh, "The Theory of Functions," p. 376. Oxford Univ. Press, London and New York, 1939; the generalization to functions of two variables is straightforward.) Thus, *any picture function is indistinguishable from an absolutely continuous function.*

We may thus assume, "up to indistinguishability," that f is continuous, which implies that it is uniformly continuous on the closure of A. Let A be subdivided into n^2 subsquares $A_{ij}^{(n)}$, defined analogously to the S_{ij}. Then, for any $\varepsilon > 0$, we can find an n such that in each $A_{ij}^{(n)}$, the value of f nowhere differs by more than ε from its value at the center of $A_{ij}^{(n)}$. Thus, if $f^{(n)}$ is the digital picture function that has this (constant) value on each $A_{ij}^{(n)}$, we have $|f - g| < \varepsilon$ at every point of A, so that *any picture function is indistinguishable from a digital picture function.*

Finally, for any $\varepsilon > 0$, we can divide up the range $[0, M]$ into intervals $[a_0, a_1), [a_1, a_2), \ldots, [a_{N-1}, a_N]$, each of length less than 2ε, where $a_0 = 0$ and $a_N = M$. Given a picture function f, define the function f_N as having the value a_k at (x, y), where a_k is the interval endpoint closest to $f(x, y)$. Thus $|f_N - f| < \varepsilon$ at every point, showing that *any picture function is indistinguishable from a quantized picture function.*

★ EXERCISE. Is any picture function indistinguishable from a binary-valued picture function? If not, why do photographs and fine-grained halftones provide acceptable renditions of gray levels? [*Hint:* We do not see the picture itself, but only a blurred version of it (see Section 6.3); if the grains of the photographic emulsion, or the halftone dots, are sufficiently tiny, the blurring averages groups of them.] Can you prove that any picture function is indistinguishable from a blurred binary-valued picture function?

1.2. Picture Processing Problems

Although pictures as defined previously are rather general mathematical objects, one would certainly not regard any mathematical operation performed on a picture function as "picture processing." For example, any square matrix with real, nonnegative elements represents a (digital) picture, but it does not follow that inverting a matrix, or computing its eigenvalues, is picture processing.

What makes picture processing a subject in its own right is that it deals with pictures that are not merely arbitrary functions or matrices, but that are pictures *of* something—which purport to represent a real scene (terrain, microscope slide, ...) or an ideal symbol (such as an alphanumeric character). It is this representational aspect that gives rise to the basic picture processing problems with which we shall be concerned in this book.

a. *Encoding and Approximation*

If pictures are not just arbitrary matrices, they do not all occur equally often. (This is certainly the case if the pictures being processed are all of one type, e.g., printed matter, aerial photographs, etc.) In terms of information theory this implies that the amount of information in an average picture is much less than if all possible pictures were equally probable. It is thus of interest to measure the information content of pictures and to devise coding schemes for representing a picture as compactly as possible; such schemes will be discussed in Chapter 2. One can also consider the possibility of approximating a picture acceptably (where the standards of acceptability may be either objective or subjective) by another picture that has lower information content. Most of the work in these areas, which is reviewed in Chapter 3, has been directed toward the goal of television bandwidth compression.

b. *Filtering, Restoration, and Enhancement*

There are many useful types of operations on pictures that are "position-invariant," i.e., whose effect on a point does not depend on its position in the picture. Such operations have properties analogous to those of time-invariant operations in electronics (Chapter 4). They can be implemented not only on conventional computers, but also in a number of other simple ways (Chapter 5), e.g., optically. Operations of this type can be used (Chapter 6) to "filter" a picture in order to detect a given pattern in it ("template matching"), to "restore" a picture that has been degraded by other such operations ("image restoration"), and to "smooth" or "sharpen" a picture ("image enhancement") to improve its "quality."

c. *Pattern Recognition and Picture Description*

In examining a picture one is very often interested only in extracting from it a description of what it depicts; this is the problem of pictorial pattern recognition. The desired description· may be merely a classification of the picture into one of a small set of prespecified classes; in this case it can often be accomplished by measuring various properties of the picture as a whole (Chapter 7). On the other hand, the description may involve properties of, and relationships among, objects that appear in the picture. To obtain such a description, it is usually necessary to explicitly locate the objects in the picture ("segmentation"; see Chapter 8) and to measure their properties (e.g., topology, size, shape, etc.; see Chapter 9) and interrelationships. Picture descriptions in terms of objects, properties, and relationships can be expressed using special "picture languages" (Chapter 10).

1.3. General References

The following collections of papers will be cited repeatedly; for brevity, they will be referred to by initials, as indicated below:

BPSS	"Biological Prototypes and Synthetic Systems" (E. E. Bernard and M. R. Kare, eds.). Plenum Press, New York, 1962.
OCR	"Optical Character Recognition" (G. L. Fischer, Jr., D. K. Pollock, B. Radack, and M. E. Stevens, eds.). Spartan, New York, 1962.
OPI	"Optical Processing of Information" (D. K. Pollock, C. J. Koester, and J. T. Tippett, eds.). Spartan, New York, 1963.
OEOIP	"Optical and Electro-Optical Information Processing" (J. T. Tippett, D. A. Berkowitz, L. C. Clapp, C. J. Koester, and A. Vanderburgh, Jr., eds.). M.I.T. Press, Cambridge, Massachusetts, 1965.
PR	"Pattern Recognition" (L. Uhr, ed.). Wiley, New York, 1966.

MPSVF   "Models for the Perception of Speech and Visual Form"
        (W. Wathen-Dunn, ed.). M.I.T. Press, Cambridge,
        Massachusetts, 1967.

PR^2 "Pattern Recognition" (L. Kanal, ed.). Thompson, Wash-
        ington, D.C., 1968.

PPR   "Pictorial Pattern Recognition" (G. C. Cheng, R. S. Ledley,
        D. K. Pollock, and A. Rosenfeld, eds.). Thompson,
        Washington, D.C., 1968.

CPR   "Conference on Pattern Recognition" (Confer. Publ. No.
        42). Inst. Elec. Engrs., London, 1968.

We shall also abbreviate *Proc. Eastern* (*Western, Fall, Spring*) *Joint Comput. Confer.* as *E(W,F,S)JCC*.

CHAPTER 2

Picture Coding

In this chapter we review the elements of discrete information theory and apply them to the case of a quantized digital picture whose gray levels are regarded as a set of "messages."

2.1. Probability and Information

Suppose that we are receiving a succession of messages from some source, and that there are only m possible messages, say $a_1, \ldots, a_m$. Even if we have no way of predicting what a given message will be, we can still estimate the *probabilities* of the messages by observing how often each message occurs; if, on the average, in a set of n messages, the message a_i occurs n_i times, we say that it has probability $p_i = n_i/n$. Thus, for each i, we have $0 \le n_i \le n$ and $n_1 + \cdots + n_m = n$, so that $0 \le p_i \le 1$ and $p_1 + \cdots + p_m = 1$. Note also that, since the messages a_i and a_j together occur $n_i + n_j$ times out of n on the average, the probability that a message will be either a_i or a_j is $(n_i + n_j)/n = p_i + p_j$. Moreover, let F be any function that associates a real number with each message; then the average value of F is $[n_1 F(a_1) + \cdots + n_m F(a_m)]/n = p_1 F(a_1) + \cdots + p_m F(a_m)$.

The amount of *information* contained in a message can be thought of as measured by the degree to which receiving it reduces our uncertainty as to what the message will be. In these terms a highly probable message contains little information, while an improbable message has a high information content. If the probability p_i is unity, the message carries zero information, while as p_i goes to zero, the information content of the message becomes arbitrarily great. A simple function of p_i that satisfies these intuitive requirements is $k \log (1/p_i)$ (or equivalently, $-k \log p_i$), where k is a positive constant; this expression is, in fact, used in information theory as the definition of "information content." The choice of k (or equivalently, of the base to which the logarithm

7

is to be taken) determines the *unit* of information; if the base is b, then a message of probability $1/b$ contains one unit of information. It is customary to choose the unit of information as corresponding to a probability of $\frac{1}{2}$, which is equivalent to taking the logarithm to the base 2; this unit is called a *bit*.

EXAMPLE. Let the message be an unknown number in the range $0, 1, \ldots,$ $2^r - 1$, so that its probability is $1/2^r$; then its information content is $\log_2 2^r = r$ bits. [In other words: An unknown r-bit number (where "bit" here means a binary digit) contains r bits of information.] Note that the number of bits of information in a message can be thought of as the number of yes-no questions that must be answered in order to completely determine the message; in the case of an r-bit number, such a set of r questions might be: "Is its first binary digit 1? Its second? ...."

If there are m possible messages with respective probabilities $p_1, \ldots, p_m$, we can measure the *average* amount of information per message by letting the function F (see at the end of the first paragraph) be the information content. This average is $-p_1 \log_2 p_1 - \cdots - p_m \log_2 p_m$ bits, or more concisely

$$- \sum_{i=1}^{m} p_i \log_2 p_i \quad \text{bits}$$

EXERCISE 1. Compute the average information per message in the following cases:

(a) $m = 4$; $\quad p_1 = p_2 = p_3 = p_4 = \frac{1}{4}$
(b) $m = 4$; $\quad p_1 = \frac{1}{2}, p_2 = \frac{1}{4}, p_3 = p_4 = \frac{1}{8}$
(c) $m = 5$; $\quad p_1 = \frac{1}{2}, p_2 = p_3 = p_4 = p_5 = \frac{1}{8}$

EXERCISE 2. Prove that if there are just two possible messages, the average information content per message is greatest if they each have probability $\frac{1}{2}$. [*Hint*: Let their probabilities be x and $1 - x$ and find the maximum of the function

$$-x \log_2 x - (1 - x) \log_2 (1 - x)]$$

★ EXERCISE 3. Prove that if there are m possible messages, the average information content per message is greatest if they each have probability $1/m$. [*Hint*: Use the method of Lagrange multipliers to find the maximum of

$$- \sum_{i=1}^{m} p_i \log_2 p_i$$

as a function of $p_1, \ldots, p_m$, subject to the constraint $p_1 + \cdots + p_m = 1$.] Note that this maximum possible average information content is just

$$\sum_{i=1}^{m} (1/m) \log_2 m = \log_2 m \quad \text{bits}$$

EXERCISE 4. Prove that if p_1 is close to 1 (so that $p_2, \ldots, p_m$ are each close to 0), the average information content per message is close to 0. [*Hint*: $-x \log_2 x$ goes to 0 as x goes to either 0 or 1.]

To apply the foregoing to pictures, we can regard a quantized digital picture as a set of messages by considering the gray level of each element as a "message." If there are m gray levels, the total amount of information in an n-by-n digital picture (which is the average amount per element times the number of elements) can be as high as $n^2 \log_2 m$ bits (see Exercise 3); the actual information content depends on the probabilities with which the gray levels occur. Physical pictorial media can be used to store information at extremely high densities (e.g., [1, 2]†). However, pictures encountered in practice (television images, line drawings, printed pages, etc.) have information contents that fall appreciably short of their potential capacities (e.g., [3, 4]), often by a factor of 2 or more. The difference between potential and actual information content is called *redundancy*.

REFERENCES

1. D. A. Lebedev, The application of information theory to photographic systems, *Zh. Nauchn. i Prikl. Fotogr. i Kinematogr.* **10**, 62–71 (January 1965); available in translation as AD 621421.‡
2. R. C. Jones, Information capacities of radiation detectors and of light, *Appl. Opt.* **2**, 351–356 (April 1963).
3. S. Deutsch, A note on some statistics concerning typewritten or printed material, *IRE Trans. Information Theory* **IT-3**, 147–148 (June 1957).
4. W. H. Foy, Jr., Entropy of simple line drawings, *IEEE Trans. Information Theory* **IT-10**, 165–167 (April 1964).

† Numbers in brackets refer to the references given at the end of the section.

‡ Documents cited by AD numbers are available to qualified requestors from the Defense Documentation Center, Cameron Station, Alexandria, Virginia; and in most cases are also for sale by the Clearinghouse for Federal Scientific and Technical Information, Springfield, Virginia.

2.2. Efficient Encoding: Single Messages

Let there be m possible messages $a_1, \ldots, a_m$ with respective probabilities $p_1, \ldots, p_m$. If we represent the messages by numbers between 0 and $m - 1$, it takes at least $\log_2 m$ binary digits to denote any given message, even if the p's are such that the average amount of information per message is far less than $\log_2 m$. (From now on, for brevity, we shall omit the subscript "2.") However, if we use a suitable code for representing the messages, we can reduce the average number of binary digits per message, in some cases to as low as the average number of bits of information per message. (It can be shown that this average is the theoretical minimum.)

The basic rule for constructing such codes is to use short binary numbers for the common messages and longer ones for the rare messages. For example, suppose that there are four messages that occur with the probabilities given in Table I. If we use the code shown in the third column of the table, the average

TABLE I

Message	Probability	Code	No. of binary digits in code
a_1	$2^{-1/4} \doteq 0.84$	1	1
a_2	$2^{-4} \doteq 0.06$	01	2
a_3	$2^{-4} \doteq 0.06$	001	3
a_4	$2^{-5} \doteq 0.03$	000	3

number of binary digits per message is

$$1(0.84) + 2(0.06) + 3(0.06) + 3(0.03) \doteq 1.23$$

which is much less than the two binary digits that would be needed if we sim-ply numbered the messages 00, 01, 10, and 11. [Note that, like the numbering, the code in Table I requires no "punctuation"; a string of binary digits representing a sequence of the messages can be "decoded" without am-biguity. If this were not the case, the code would actually involve three sym-bols (0, 1, and a "punctuation" symbol for separating the messages), and so would require the equivalent of considerably more than 1.23 binary digits per message.]

In the above example, the average number of binary digits of code per message is still not as low as the average amount of information per message, which is

$$\tfrac{1}{4}(0.84) + 8(0.06) + 5(0.03) \doteq 0.84 \quad \text{bits}$$

It is sometimes possible to construct a simple code that is near optimum in the sense of requiring nearly as few binary digits per message as the average number of bits of information per message. One way of doing this is to subdivide the messages into two groups, then each group into two subgroups, and so on until each subgroup contains only a single message; where at each subdivision step, the probabilities of the two (sub)groups are as equal as possible. The code is then defined as follows: If a message is in the first group, the first binary digit of its code is 0; if it is in the second group, this digit is 1. In either case if the message is in the first subgroup of its group, the second binary digit of its code is 0, and if in the second subgroup, 1; and so on. An optimum code of this type is illustrated in Table II.

TABLE II

Message	Probability	Code
a_1	$\tfrac{1}{2}$	0
a_2	$\tfrac{1}{4}$	10
a_3	$\tfrac{1}{8}$	110
a_4	$\tfrac{1}{8}$	111

For this particular set of probabilities, the code actually requires an average number of binary digits per message equal to the average number of bits of information per message, which is 1.75. Codes of this type are known as Shannon–Fano–Huffman codes.

EXERCISE 1. Generalize the example just given as follows: Let there be m messages $a_1, \ldots, a_m$ with respective probabilities $1/2, 1/4, 1/8, \ldots, 1/2^{m-2}$, $1/2^{m-1}, 1/2^{m-1}$. Construct a code, as previously described, by dividing the messages into the subgroups shown in Table III. (Since, at each step, the first subgroup has only a single element, only the second subgroup need be further subdivided at the next step.) Verify that the average number of binary digits per message in this code is the same as the average number of bits of information per message, namely, $(2^m - 1)/2^{m-1}$.

11

TABLE III

Step	First subgroup	Second subgroup
1	a_1	$a_2, \ldots, a_m$
2	a_2	$a_3, \ldots, a_m$
.	.	.
.	.	.
.	.	.
$m-1$	a_{m-1}	a_m

★ EXERCISE 2. Show that unless the probabilities of the m messages (in some order) are as in Exercise 1, any code constructed by dividing the messages into subgroups (as described in the text) requires more binary digits per message than $(2^m - 1)/2^{m-1}$.

2.3. Efficient Encoding: Sequences of Messages

If we know that the message a_i has just been received, the probability that the next message will be a_j is not necessarily p_j, since the successive messages may be interdependent. Let us denote the *conditional probability* $p(a_j \mid a_i)$ (read "the probability that a message is a_j, given that the preceding message was a_i") by p_{ij}. (If $p_{ij} = p_j$ for all i and j, we say that the messages are *independent*.) Evidently, for each i, we have $p_{i1} + \cdots + p_{im} = 1$, since *some* message must follow a_i.

In a set of n pairs of successive messages, on the average, the number of pairs in which the first message is a_i will be $n_i = p_i n$, and of these n_i messages, the number in which the second message is a_j will be $p_{ij} n_i = p_i p_{ij} n$; thus the probability of the pair of messages (a_i, a_j) is $p_i p_{ij}$. Hence, on the average, the number of pairs of messages in which the second message is a_j will be

$$p_1 p_{1j} n + p_2 p_{2j} n + \cdots + p_m p_{mj} n$$

so that the probability that the second message of a pair will be a_j is $p_1 p_{1j} + \cdots + p_m p_{mj}$. Now, any message but the very first one can be regarded as the second message of a pair; thus, in a long sequence of messages, the total number of times that a_j occurs is approximately the same as the number of times that a_j occurs as the second message of a pair. It follows that in a long sequence, we have (approximately)

$$p_j \doteq p_1 p_{1j} + \cdots + p_m p_{mj}$$

for each j. One can solve this set of equations for the p_j's in terms of the p_{ij}'s. For example, suppose that $m = 2$; then

$$p_1 \doteq p_1 p_{11} + p_2 p_{21}$$

and since $p_2 = 1 - p_1$, while $p_{12} = 1 - p_{11}$, this readily gives us

$$p_1 \doteq p_{21}/(p_{12} + p_{21}); \qquad p_2 \doteq p_{12}/(p_{12} + p_{21})$$

(Note that the argument breaks down if $p_{12} = p_{21} = 0$; but in this case the first message of the sequence repeats indefinitely, while the other one never occurs, so that we have either $p_1 = 1, p_2 = 0$, or vice versa.)

EXERCISE 1. Carry out the solution for the p_j's in terms of the p_{ij}'s for arbitrary m. In what cases does the solution break down?

★ EXERCISE 2. Generalize the above discussion to k-tuples of successive messages, using *higher-order conditional probabilities* $p(a_j | a_{i1}, \ldots, a_{i, k-1})$ (read "the probability that a message is a_j, given that the $k - 1$ preceding messages, in sequence, were $a_{i1}, \ldots, a_{i, k-1}$").

In the following paragraphs, we describe three important approaches to economically encoding a sequence of interdependent messages.

a. *Block Coding*

If the successive messages are independent of one another, then by the first paragraph above, the probability of any pair (a_i, a_j) is just $p_i p_j$. It follows that the average information content of a pair of messages is

$$-p_1{}^2 \log p_1{}^2 - p_1 p_2 \log p_1 p_2 - \cdots - p_1 p_m \log p_1 p_m$$

$$-p_2 p_1 \log p_2 p_1 - p_2{}^2 \log p_2{}^2 - \cdots - p_2 p_m \log p_2 p_m$$

$$\vdots$$

$$-p_m p_1 \log p_m p_1 - p_m p_2 \log p_m p_2 - \cdots - p_m{}^2 \log p_m{}^2$$

Since $\log p_i p_j = \log p_i + \log p_j$, this reduces to

$$-p_1(p_1 + \cdots + p_m) \log p_1 - p_1 [p_1 \log p_1 + \cdots + p_m \log p_m]$$
$$-p_2(p_1 + \cdots + p_m) \log p_2 - p_2 [p_1 \log p_1 + \cdots + p_m \log p_m]$$
$$\vdots$$
$$-p_m(p_1 + \cdots + p_m) \log p_m - p_m [p_1 \log p_1 + \cdots + p_m \log p_m]$$

where the bracketed expression on each line is just the average information content per individual message, call it I. Now in the first term on each line, the second factor is 1, so that these terms add up to I; while the second terms also add up to $(p_1 + \cdots + p_m)I = I$, proving that the average information content of a pair of messages is just $2I$.

EXERCISE 3. Show that, in general, if the probability of any k-tuple of successive messages is just the product of the probabilities of its terms, then the average information content in a k-tuple of messages is kI.

The foregoing shows that nothing is gained by grouping independent messages into pairs (or analogously, by Exercise 3, into k-tuples, for any k); no reduction in the total amount of information in a sequence of messages can be achieved in this way. If the messages are not independent, however, it may be advantageous to compute their average information content by grouping them into "blocks" (e.g., pairs) rather than by treating them on an individual basis. For example, suppose that there are just two possible messages; then, by the results of the beginning of the section, the probabilities $(p_i p_{ij})$ of the four possible pairs of messages (a_i, a_j) are approximately given by Table IV. In particular, suppose that $p_{12} = p_{21} = p$. Then $p_1 \doteq p_{21}/(p_{12} + p_{21}) = \frac{1}{2}$, and similarly $p_2 \doteq \frac{1}{2}$, so that the average information content of the individual messages in the sequence, ignoring their interdependency, is one

TABLE IV

i	j	Probability of (a_i, a_j)
1	1	$p_{21} p_{11}/(p_{12} + p_{21})$
1	2	$p_{21} p_{12}/(p_{12} + p_{21})$
2	1	$p_{12} p_{21}/(p_{12} + p_{21})$
2	2	$p_{12} p_{22}/(p_{12} + p_{21})$

bit. The pairs of messages, on the other hand, are not equally probable; in fact the average information content of a pair of messages is readily $1 - p \log p - (1 - p) \log (1 - p)$, which (for p close to 0 or close to 1) can be nearly as low as one bit. Thus if the messages are treated a pair at a time, the average information content per single message may turn out to be nearly as low as half a bit.

★ EXERCISE 4. Generalize the foregoing to arbitrary m and to higher-order conditional probabilities.

b. *Predictive Coding*

Another way of capitalizing on message interdependency is to use it to predict each message from the preceding one(s), and to take the differences between the predicted and actual messages as a new set of messages. For example, if the predicted message was a_i and the actual message is a_j, the "difference" can be represented by

$$j - i \quad \text{if} \quad j \geq i$$
$$j - i + m \quad \text{if} \quad j < i$$

Thus there are only m possible differences $0, \ldots, m - 1$; and if we know that the subscript of the predicted message was i and the "difference" was h, the subscript of the actual message is uniquely determined as

$$i + h \quad \text{if} \quad i + h \leq m$$
$$i + h - m \quad \text{if} \quad i + h > m$$

It follows that the sequence of messages is completely determined by specifying the first message and the sequence of "differences." The advantage of replacing the given messages by "difference messages" is that if the original messages are interdependent, the difference messages may have considerably lower average information content per message than the originals.

To illustrate these ideas, let us again consider the case in which there are just two messages. Suppose that we use the simple prediction rule that each message is the same as the preceding message. Thus the probability that a difference will be 0 is just the probability that a pair of successive messages will be either (a_1, a_1) or (a_2, a_2), while the probability of the difference 1 is the same as the probability that a pair will be (a_1, a_2) or (a_2, a_1). Using the

15

probabilities of the pairs from Table IV, we thus see that the difference messages 0 and 1 have respective probabilites

$$(p_{11}p_{21} + p_{12}p_{22})/(p_{12} + p_{21}) \quad \text{and} \quad 2p_{12}p_{21}/(p_{12} + p_{21})$$

In particular suppose, as we did in the case of block coding, that $p_{12} = p_{21} = p$; then $p_1 \doteq p_2 \doteq \frac{1}{2}$, but the probabilities of the difference messages are $1 - p$ and p, respectively. Thus the average information content per difference message can be arbitrarily low, even though the original messages have an information content of about one bit each.

EXERCISE 5. Generalize this example.

> More generally, suppose that we perform an invertible operation on the original set of messages (in the foregoing case, "subtraction" of successive messages), so that the original messages can be reconstructed by applying the inverse operation. Then we can try to choose the operation in such a way as to capitalize on interdependencies in the original messages, so that the new messages have very low average information content.

c. *Run Coding*

In the example given in Table IV (where $p_{12} = p_{21} = p$), the average information content per message (pair or difference) is low when p is small, i.e., when there is a high probability that any given message will be repeated rather than being followed by a different message. In such a case there is a tendency for long "runs" of repeated messages to occur. A similar tendency can occur even with independent messages if one of the messages is much more probable than all the others put together (e.g., the first example in Section 2.2); in such cases the highly probable message tends to occur in runs, the other messages in isolation. If this tendency is sufficiently strong, it may be more economical to encode the first message of each run and the *length* of the run, or the first message of each run and its *position* in the sequence of messages, rather than encoding every message in the sequence. Evidently, this information completely determines the sequence. [If there are only two possible messages, it even suffices to specify the first message in the sequence and the lengths (or positions of first elements) of all the runs, since runs of the two messages must alternate.] These two schemes are called *run length coding* and *run end coding*, respectively.

As an illustration of how a sequence of messages can be economically encoded using run coding methods, suppose that there are just two possible messages and that the length of the sequence is n, while the average run length is $r > \log n$. A complete description of the sequence in terms of run ends then requires only about $(n/r) \log n$ bits (namely, $\log n$ bits to specify the position of each of approximately n/r runs), which is less than the n bits required to specify the sequence if no coding is used.

★ EXERCISE 6. What is the average run length in the case of two interdependent messages? In the case of two independent messages? Generalize.

★ EXERCISE 7. Compare the economies that can be achieved in the example given in Table IV (where $p_{12} = p_{21} = p$) by using block coding, predictive coding, and run coding, as a function of p.

REFERENCES

1. E. R. Kretzmer, Statistics of television signals, *Bell System Tech. J.* **31**, 751–763 (July 1952).
2. W. F. Schreiber, The measurement of third order probability distributions of television signals, *IRE Trans. Information Theory* **IT-2**, 94–105 (September 1956).
3. P. R. Wallace, Real time measurement of element differences in television programs, *Proc. IEEE* **54**, 1576–1577 (November 1966).

   Of related interest is S. Nishikawa, R. J. Massa, and J. C. Mott-Smith, Area properties of television pictures, *IEEE Trans. Information Theory* **IT-11**, 348–352 (July 1965).

2.4. Some Additional Remarks on Encoding

In principle it is possible to employ encoding schemes that can automatically change the code being used in order to match it to the statistics of the information being encoded. Similarly, if there are more than two possible messages, so that the messages can be represented by binary numbers having more than one digit, the statistics of the digits will often not be the same (e.g., the more significant digits may change less often from message to message than do the less significant ones). It may thus be advantageous to use a different code for each of the digits. This latter approach is known as *bit plane encoding.*

EXERCISE. Construct an example in which bit plane encoding yields a saving in average information content per message.

If a picture contains only a few regions, each having a constant gray level and a simple geometrical description, it can be very economically encoded by giving its *description*, i.e., by specifying the geometry and gray level of each region. For example, a binary-valued *n*-by-*n* digital picture, in which the elements in a subrectangle are 1's and all other elements are 0's, can be completely described by specifying the coordinates of two opposite corners of the rectangle; each of these four coordinates requires just log *n* bits. [Run coding can be thought of as the special case of this type of encoding, in which (if the usual raster scan is used) the "regions" are horizontal line segments.] "Line drawings" can often be encoded very compactly in this way, especially if they involve only curves and arcs of constant thickness that have simple equations (e.g., straight lines or conic sections). This approach is used in all *computer graphics* systems, since it not only compresses the pictures but also makes it especially easy to perform geometrical operations on them.

REFERENCE

1. J. W. Schwartz and R. C. Barker, Bit plane encoding: a technique for source encoding, *IEEE Trans. Aerospace Electronic Systems* **AES-2**, 385–392 (July 1966).

  For other references on picture encoding, see the bibliographies on television bandwidth compression cited at the beginning of the next section.

CHAPTER 3

Approximation of Pictures

For many purposes, one has no need of all of the details that appear in a picture; two pictures that look sufficiently alike can be regarded as identical. Moreover, it is often possible to replace a given picture by a simpler picture that looks like it but that has lower information content. The degree of "compression" that can be obtained by approximation methods is generally greater than that obtainable by encoding techniques. On the other hand, approximation may degrade the picture, while encoding preserves it exactly.

In this chapter we survey techniques for picture compression by approximation. Any of the standard methods used to approximate functions can be applied to picture functions. In addition there exist techniques that are specifically picture-oriented, capitalizing on properties of the visual perception process to achieve approximations that are acceptable but which have significantly reduced information contents. This latter work has been primarily directed toward television bandwidth compression.†

Two basic tools that can be used in the approximation of a function are *sampling* and *quantization*. In sampling one takes values of the function at a finite set of points and approximates the function by *interpolating* pieces of analytically simple functions through these values. In quantization one allows the function to take on only a finite set of values ("quantization levels"), replacing the actual value at each point by the quantization level closest to it. The sample points and/or quantization levels can be prespecified, or they can depend on the nature of the function, as described in the following sections.

Another approach to approximating a function, which can also be usefully applied to picture approximation, is to expand the function in some type of series [e.g., Taylor series, Fourier series (or, more

---

† It should be pointed out that, in the case of television, there are significant possibilities for bandwidth compression based on the fact that *successive frames* generally differ by relatively little; however, this approach will not be considered here.

generally, series expansion in terms of a given set of orthogonal functions), expansion of a matrix as a sum of dyads, etc.] and to use the sum of the first few terms of the series as an approximation.

GENERAL REFERENCES

1. T. S. Huang, Digital picture coding, *Proc. Nat. Electron. Confer.* **22**, 793–797 (1966).
2. W. E. Pratt, A bibliography on television bandwidth reduction techniques, *IEEE Trans. Information Theory* **IT-13**, 114–115 (January 1967); see also the addenda in A. Rosenfeld, Bandwidth reduction bibliography, *ibid.* **IT-14**, 601–602 (July 1968).
3. Special issue on redundancy reduction, *Proc. IEEE* **55**, 251–406 (March 1967).

3.1. Sampling (Prespecified Sample Points)

The simplest class of sampling methods for approximating a function is that in which the sample points are prespecified. It is usually simplest to choose the points to be equally spaced, so that they form a regular array. However, it may sometimes be desirable to use unequally spaced points. For example, if the scale varies across a photograph because of perspective, one might want to pick sample points at a spacing that varies with the scale, so that the points are equally spaced with respect to the original scene.

a. *Polynomial Interpolation*

Given a set of samples of a picture function, one can use simple functions of various types to approximate the picture by interpolation between the sample points. The simplest functions that can be used for this purpose are the constant functions; here, the picture is divided into neighborhoods, each containing one sample point, and the gray level of the approximation picture in each neighborhood is taken to be equal to the gray level at the corresponding sample point. Note that, if the sample points form a regular n-by-n Cartesian array, and the neighborhoods are taken to be the subsquares S_{ij} (Section 1.1), then the approximation picture is just the n-by-n digital picture defined by the matrix of gray levels at the sample points; thus *digitization* can be regarded as a "zero-order" sampling and interpolation method of approximating a picture.

More generally, one can "fit" pieces of planes, or of higher-order (e.g., polynomial) surfaces, to the values of a picture function at a given set of sample points. For example, if we imagine that the sample points are connected to their neighbors, forming a network of triangles, we can find a plane that contains the gray levels at the vertices of each triangle, and in this way construct a continuous polyhedral surface, having triangular facets, that passes through all of the sample-point gray levels. If higher-order surfaces are used for interpolation instead of planes, one can require each piece of surface to pass through a larger number of sample-point gray levels; alternatively, one can try to constrain the pieces to agree, not only in gray level, but also in the values of various derivatives, along their curves of intersection, so that the resulting interpolated surface is not only continuous but also "smooth."

b. *Sinusoidal Interpolation: The Sampling Theorem*

The functions used for interpolation need not be polynomials; families of transcendental functions, such as exponentials, sinusoids, etc., can also be used. Sinusoidal interpolation is of special interest because of an important result, known as the *sampling theorem*, which states that under certain conditions, this type of interpolation can exactly reconstruct the original function. (A precise statement of this theorem, and a proof for the case of a function of one variable, are given in the appendix to this chapter.)

c. *Some Additional Remarks on Interpolation*

It is sometimes convenient to break up the process of interpolating between given sample values into two steps, by first computing interpolated values at a new set of points and then interpolating pieces of functions between these points. For example, one might do this in order to refine a given coarse array of sample points, or to replace a given irregular array by a regular one; this has the potential advantages that interpolation on a regular array may be simpler, and that if the array is made sufficiently fine, very "low-order" interpolation schemes may become acceptable. To compute an interpolated value at a given new point, one would typically take a weighted average of the values at nearby sample points (e.g., those within a specified distance, or a specified number of nearest ones), with the weights depending on their distances from the given point.

21

Since interpolation of functions of two variables is a relatively complicated process, pictures are often approximated by interpolating in each coordinate separately. In particular, in the case of television images, it is especially convenient to choose the sample points along the television raster lines, and to interpolate along and across the lines.

EXERCISE. Let $f(x, y) = (r^2 - x^2 - y^2)^{1/2}$, a hemisphere of radius r with center at the origin. Compute the maximum and average differences between f and the approximations to f, obtained using the sample points with integer coordinates, and the following types of interpolation: (a) zero-order, where the approximating function is constant on the unit squares centered at the sample points; (b) first-order, using pieces of planes through triples of adjacent sample points; (c) one-dimensional linear interpolation, first in x, then in y; ★(d) the first k terms of the Fourier series expansion of f in the square $-r \leq x, y \leq r$.

3.2. Quantization (Prespecified Levels)

In order that a quantized picture be acceptable, it may sometimes be necessary to use the order of 100 quantization levels. Such a fine degree of quantization is particularly important if we are quantizing a region in a picture across which the gray level changes slowly. In this situation large parts of the region will be quantized to constant gray levels, while between these parts, there will be curves along which there is an abrupt gray-level jump. These curves will tend to appear as conspicuous "false contours," cutting across the region, and may make the quantized approximation to the original picture unacceptable, since they define spurious "objects," which may compete with or conceal the real objects shown in the picture. The effect of reducing the number of quantization levels is shown in Figure 3.1. (In each case shown, the levels span approximately the same range, and each point is given the level closest to the one that it had in the 32-level picture.)

As in the case of sampling, it is usually simplest to choose quantization levels that are evenly spaced; but unequally spaced levels may sometimes be preferable. For example, suppose that the gray levels in a certain range occur frequently, while the others occur rarely. In such a case one might wish to use quantization levels that are finely spaced inside this range and coarsely spaced outside it; this increases the average accuracy of the quantization

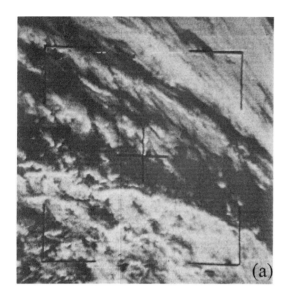

Figure 3.1. Effect of reducing the number of quantization levels in a digitized picture. (a) Thirty-two levels.

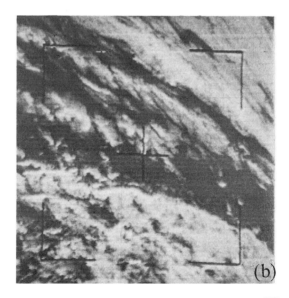

Figure 3.1. (b) Sixteen levels.

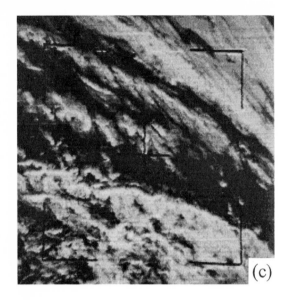

Figure 3.1. (c) Eight levels.

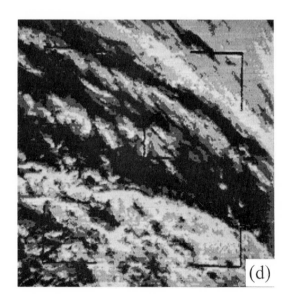

Figure 3.1. (d) Four levels.

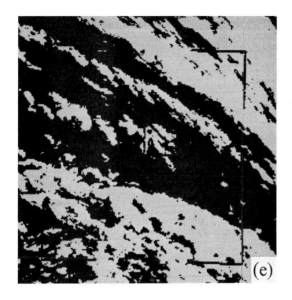

Figure 3.1. (e) Two levels.

without increasing the number of levels. This method is known as *tapered quantization*; it is illustrated in Figure 3.2.

In quantizing a picture it may even be desirable to introduce some degree of randomness into the quantization process. For example, false contours can be "broken up" by randomly shifting the quantization levels up and down from point to point, or equivalently, by adding random noise to the picture before quantizing it, so that the loci at which the quantization jumps occur are no longer smooth curves. In practice one can use noise that is "pseudorandom" (i.e., deterministic but highly discontinuous) rather than random. The identical "noise" pattern can then be resubtracted from the picture when it is "unquantized" and displayed. This approach is illustrated in Figure 3.3.

See L. G. Roberts, Picture coding using pseudorandom noise, *IRE Trans. Information Theory* **IT-8**, 145–154 (February 1962). In general the number of quantization levels required for acceptability can be reduced by appropriate *prefiltering* and *postfiltering*, i.e., by suitably modifying the picture before and after quantizing it.

25

Figure 3.2. "Tapered" quantization.
(a) Sixteen equally spaced levels. (b) Sixteen tapered levels. (c) Four equally spaced levels. (d) Four tapered levels.

Reprinted from T. S. Huang, O. J. Tretiak. B. T. Prasada, and Y. Yamaguchi, Design considerations in PCM transmission of low-resolution monochrome still pictures, *Proc. IEEE* **55**, 333 (March 1967).

Figure 3.3. Quantization (to 8 levels) using pseudorandom noise.

Reprinted from T. S. Huang, O. J. Tretiak, B. T. Prasada, and Y. Yamaguchi, Design considerations in PCM transmission of low-resolution monochrome still pictures, *Proc. IEEE* **55**, 333 (March 1967).

EXERCISE. What is the average "error" if the hemisphere

$$f(x, y) = (r^2 - x^2 - y^2)^{\frac{1}{2}}$$

is quantized to k equally spaced levels? How should the levels be tapered to minimize the average error?

3.3. Variable Sampling and Quantization

The choice of sample points or quantization levels need not be pre-specified; it can be made to depend on the nature of the pictures being approximated. In particular this can sometimes be done in such a way as to take advantage of the observer's visual limitations with respect to what he is willing to accept as an adequate approximation. For example, the eye is relatively poor at estimating the gray levels immediately adjacent to a sharp "edge" on a picture, so that coarse quantization can be used near such edges. On the other hand, in a "smooth" region on the picture, if too few quantization levels are used, the transitions from level to level will show up conspicuously as false contours. Conversely, in sampling, closely spaced samples are required in the vicinity of a sharp edge to preserve its shape, whereas coarse sampling is generally adequate in a smooth region. Thus, when quantizing or sampling a picture, one might test each point for the presence of an edge (on "edge detection" criteria see Section 6.5); one could then use coarse quantization at edges (but in such a way as to ensure that the two sides of the edge remain at different gray levels) and coarse sampling away from edges. (Note that with regard to quantization, a similar result could be obtained by using tapered quantization of the *differences* between the gray levels of successive points on the picture,† with coarse quantization being used for large differences and fine quantization for small ones.)

> In terms of television transmission, one can transmit the low-frequency and high-frequency parts of the picture signal separately, with different approximation (and encoding) schemes used for each of the two; or one can transmit the low-frequency picture signal as well as the positions (and approximate contrasts) of the edges in the picture, so that synthetic edges can be added to the received picture. For an example of such a "two-channel" approach, see Figure 3.4.

† This tacitly assumes a digitized picture that is being systematically scanned.

27

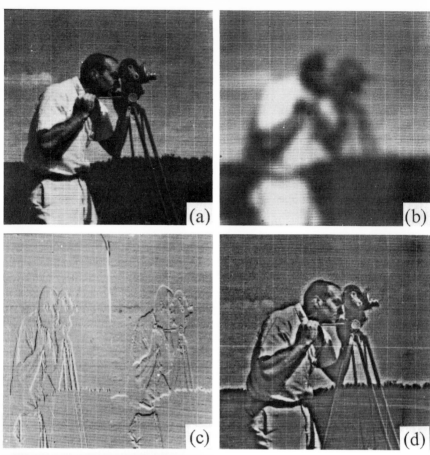

Figure 3.4. A "two-channel" approximation scheme. (a) Original picture. (b) Low-frequency version. (c) Edges ($\partial/\partial x$ and $\partial/\partial y$). (d) High-frequency version synthesized from edges. (e) Reconstructed picture [combining (b) and (d)].

Reprinted from T. S. Huang and O. J. Tretiak, Research in picture processing, "Optical and Electro-Optical Information Processing" (J. T. Tippett, D. A. Berkowitz, L. C. Clapp, C. J. Koester, and A. Vanderburgh, Jr., eds.), by permission of The M.I.T. Press, Cambridge, Massachusetts, 1965.

Another approach to variable sampling is to select sample points as far apart as possible, so that the (maximum, or perhaps, average) difference between the original and interpolated functions does not exceed a prespecified amount; alternatively, one can select a prespecified number of sample points in such a way as to minimize this difference. (Ordinary quantization can be regarded as a zero-order case in which a prespecified set of constant functions, namely, the quantization levels, are used for interpolation.) There are many variations on this approach, but since these methods are not specific to picture functions, they will not be reviewed here in detail.

EXERCISE 1. How many sample points are needed to approximate the hemisphere $f(x, y) = (r^2 - x^2 - y^2)^{1/2}$ [using each of the interpolation schemes (a)–(c) in the exercise at the end of Section 3.1], so that the maximum (average) error is r/k?

★ EXERCISE 2. Where should k sample points be chosen to give the best approximation to this hemisphere? Use each of the interpolation schemes (a)–(c) in the exercise at the end of Section 3.1.

REFERENCES

1. T. S. Huang and O. J. Tretiak, Research in picture processing, OEOIP, pp. 45–57.
2. R. S. Simpson, C. A. Blackwell, and W. O. Frost, Compendium of redundancy removal processes, *IEEE Trans. Aerospace Electronic Systems* **AES-2**, 471–474 (July 1966).
3. L. D. Davisson, The theoretical analysis of data compression systems, *Proc. IEEE* **56**, 176–186 (February 1968).

3.4. Approximation of Line Drawings

A "line drawing" can be completely described by specifying a finite set of curves and arcs. As pointed out in Section 2.4, if these curves have analytically simple descriptions, a very concise description of such a picture is possible. Even if they do not, one can still approximate the picture by fitting pieces of analytically simple curves to the actual curves. Here again, either fixed or variable sampling procedures can be used, as described below. In either case the curve can be approximated by interpolating straight-line segments, or pieces of higher-order curves, between the sample points. The former method yields a *polygonal* approximation, while the latter can be made to yield a "smooth" approximation if the pieces of curve are matched in slope, curvature, etc. at their common endpoints.

a. *Fixed Sampling*

A curve can be approximated by using a set of sample points chosen from a fixed (e.g., regular Cartesian) array of points in the plane. For example (see Figure 3.5), one can use those points of the array which have the property

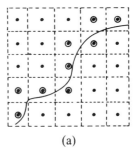

(a)

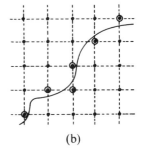

Figure 3.5. Methods of approximating a curve by points from a fixed array. (a) Square neighborhoods. (b) Gridline neighborhoods.

(b)

that the curve passes through some prespecified neighborhood of them. In particular one can imagine the points of the array as joined by a grid of lines, and each time the curve crosses one of the lines, one can use the point of the array that lies closest to this intersection point. (This amounts to taking the part of the grid closest to each of the points as the "neighborhood" of that

30

point.) In the polygonal approximations obtained in this way, each side of the approximating polygon is either horizontal or vertical and of unit length, or diagonal and of length $\sqrt{2}$; thus this polygon is completely determined by specifying its starting point and the sequence of slopes of its sides. This type of polygonal approximation [1] is known as *chain encoding*. (Another approach to fixed sampling is to choose sample points that lie *on the curve* at a prespecified spacing.)

b. *Variable Sampling*

As indicated in the previous section, another method of approximating a curve is to choose sample points so that the difference between the original and interpolated curves does not exceed a prespecified amount; alternatively, one can select a prespecified number of sample points to minimize this difference. In either case one might or might not require the sample points to lie on the curve. If a polygonal approximation is required, and the number of sample points is limited, it is evident that the best places to put the sample points are near points where the curve has a high curvature [2].

Approximation of curves provides an interesting alternative approach to the approximation of surfaces (i.e., picture functions): One can construct a *contour map* of the surface and approximate the contour lines [3].

EXERCISE. Formulate and solve analogs of the exercises at the ends of Sections 3.1 and 3.3 for the circle $x^2 + y^2 = r^2$. Which of the two methods of chain encoding illustrated in Figure 3.5 gives a better approximation to this circle? (Use the array of points with integer coordinates.)

REFERENCES

1. H. Freeman, On the encoding of arbitrary geometric configurations, *IRE Trans. Electronic Computers* **EC-10**, 260–268 (June 1961).
2. F. Attneave, Some informational aspects of visual perception, *Psychol. Rev.* **61**, 183–193 (1954).
3. B. W. Boehm, Tabular representations of multivariate functions—with applications to topographic modeling, *Proc. ACM Nat. Confer.* pp. 403–415 (August 1967).

Appendix: Proof of the Sampling Theorem

This appendix makes use of the definition and invertibility property of the Fourier transform (Section 4.3). It also makes use of the well-known fact that if $g(t)$ is a sufficiently well-behaved function on the interval $-b \leq t \leq b$, it can be expanded in a *Fourier series*:

$$g(t) = \sum_{k=-\infty}^{\infty} a_k e^{\pi jkt/b}$$

where $j = \sqrt{-1}$, and

$$a_k = \frac{1}{2b} \int_{-b}^{b} e^{-\pi jkt/b} g(t)\, dt$$

where $k = 0, \pm 1, \ldots$.
Here the sum of the series is a periodic function with period $2b$, which agrees with g on the interval.

THEOREM 1. Let f be a function of one variable whose Fourier transform is zero outside the interval $-b \leq w_t \leq b$; then f can be exactly reconstructed from samples of its values taken $1/2b$ apart or closer.

PROOF. Let $F(w_t) = \int_{-\infty}^{\infty} e^{2\pi jw_t t} f(t)\, dt$ be the Fourier transform of f; by hypothesis, we have $F(w_t) = 0$ for $|w_t| > b$. Let $F(w_t) = \sum_{-\infty}^{\infty} a_k e^{\pi jkw_t/b}$ be the Fourier series expansion of F in the interval $-b \leq w_t \leq b$; thus

$$a_k = \frac{1}{2b} \int_{-b}^{b} e^{-\pi jkw_t/b} F(w_t)\, dw_t \tag{1}$$

But f is the inverse Fourier transform of F, so that

$$f(t) = \int_{-\infty}^{\infty} e^{-2\pi jw_t t} F(w_t)\, dw_t = \int_{-b}^{b} e^{-2\pi jw_t t} F(w_t)\, dw_t \tag{2}$$

Comparing (1) and (2), we see that $a_k = f(k/2b)/2b$, so that $F(w_t) = (1/2b) \sum_{-\infty}^{\infty} f(k/2b) e^{\pi jkw_t/b}$, and we have

$$f(t) = \frac{1}{2b} \sum_{-\infty}^{\infty} f\left(\frac{k}{2b}\right) \left[\int_{-b}^{b} e^{\pi jw_t((k/b) - 2t)}\, dw_t \right]$$

$$= \sum_{-\infty}^{\infty} f\left(\frac{k}{2b}\right) \frac{\sin[\pi b((k/b) - 2t)]}{\pi b((k/b) - 2t)}$$

which gives $f(t)$ in terms of its sample values $f(k/2b)$. Note that if we had expanded F in a Fourier series over an interval larger than $-b \leq w_t \leq b$, the result would have been a reconstruction of f from samples closer together than $1/2b$. ∎

For functions of two variables, it can be shown analogously that the following theorem holds:

THEOREM 2. Let f be a function of two variables whose Fourier transform F is zero outside a bounded subset S of the plane. Let (a, b) and (c, d) be any points such that, for any two pairs of integers (m, n) and (p, q), the sets obtained by shifting S by the amounts $(m(a + c)$, $n(b + d))$ and $(p(a + c), q(b + d))$, respectively, have no point in common. [Here, the parallelogram defined by the vectors (a, b) and (c, d) plays a role analogous to that of the interval $[-b, b]$ in Theorem 1.] Let (s, t) and (u, v) be such that $as + bt = cu + dv = 2\pi$; $au + bv = cs + dt = 0$. Then f can be exactly reconstructed from samples of its values taken at the points $(hs + ku, ht + kv)$, where h and k are integers.

It should be pointed out that, in practice, F will only be *close* to zero outside S; as a result, the reconstruction of f from its samples will not be exact.

REFERENCES

1. D. P. Petersen and D. Middleton, Sampling and reconstruction of wave–number-limited functions in n-dimensional Euclidean spaces, *Information and Control* **5**, 279–323 (1962).
2. R. T. Prosser, A multidimensional sampling theorem, *J. Math. Anal. Appl.* **16**, 574–584 (1966).
3. G. C. Cheng and R. S. Ledley, A theory of picture digitization and applications, PPR, pp. 329–352.
4. W. D. Montgomery, Reconstruction of pictures from scanned records, *IEEE Trans. Information Theory* **IT-11**, 204–206 (April 1965).

CHAPTER 4

Position-Invariant Operations
on Pictures: 1, Theory

In this and the next two chapters we study various types of useful operations that are performed on pictures "uniformly," in other words, whose effect on a point does not depend on the position of the point in the picture.

4.1. Position-Invariant Operations

Let $\mathscr{S}$ be the set of functions of two real variables that are defined on the entire plane. Let ϕ be a function from $\mathscr{S}$ into itself; we shall call ϕ an *operation* on $\mathscr{S}$. Let $T_{u,\,v}$ ["translation by (u, v)"] be the "shifting operation" on $\mathscr{S}$ defined by

$$[T_{u,v}(f)](x, y) = f(x - u, y - v)$$

for all f in $\mathscr{S}$ and all (x, y) in the plane.† We shall call ϕ a *position-invariant operation* if it commutes with every $T_{u,\,v}$; in other words, if we have

$$\phi(T_{u,\,v}(f)) = T_{u,\,v}(\phi(f))$$

for all f in $\mathscr{S}$ and all (u, v) in the plane.

Position-invariant operations are the two-dimensional analogs of *time-invariant operations*, which are studied in electronics.

The following are some important special types of position-invariant operations:

† Here "$[T_{u,\,v}(f)](x, y)$" means "the function $T_{u,\,v}(f)$ evaluated at the point (x, y)."

a. *Shifting Operations*

The shifting operations themselves are position-invariant, since they commute with one another. In fact

$$[T_{r,s}(T_{u,v}(f))](x, y) = [T_{u,v}(f)](x - r, y - s) = f((x - r) - u, (y - s) - v)$$
$$= f((x - u) - r, (y - v) - s) = [T_{r,s}(f)](x - u, y - v)$$
$$= [T_{u,v}(T_{r,s}(f))](x, y)$$

for all r, s, u, v, and f. It is evident that other types of geometrical operations, such as rotations, scale changes, etc., are not, in general, position-invariant.

★ EXERCISE 1. Let ϕ be the geometrical operation defined by $[\phi(f)](x, y) = f(\xi(x, y), \eta(x, y))$. Can ϕ be position-invariant if it is not a translation?

b. *Point Operations*

Suppose that ϕ is such that $[\phi(f)](x, y)$ depends only on $f(x, y)$; in other words, suppose that there exists a function h of *one* real variable such that $[\phi(f)](x, y) = h(f(x, y))$ for all f in $\mathscr{S}$ and all (x, y) in the plane. We shall call such a ϕ a *point operation*. Readily, a point operation is position-invariant; in fact, for all (x, y) and (u, v) in the plane, and all f in $\mathscr{S}$, we have $[\phi(T_{u,v}(f))](x, y) = h([T_{u,v}(f)](x, y)) = h(f(x - u, y - v)) = [\phi(f)](x - u, y - v) = [T_{u,v}(\phi(f))](x, y)$.

In terms of pictures a point operation changes the gray level at each point in a manner that does not depend on the rest of the picture. Thus, a point operation modifies the gray scale without changing the geometry of the picture. Examples of such operations include "intensification" and "attenuation" (multiplication of the gray scale by a constant), "gamma correction" of the gray scale, and quantization.

c. *Local Operations*

More generally, suppose that $[\phi(f)](x, y)$ depends only on the values of f in some neighborhood $N(x, y)$, where N is the same neighborhood for all (x, y) in the plane; i.e., for any u and v, $N(x - u, y - v)$ is just the set of points $(z - u, w - v)$ such that (z, w) is in $N(x, y)$. In this case we call ϕ a *local operation*; readily, such an operation is position-invariant. Note that a point operation is a special case of a local operation, namely, that in which the neighborhood consists of just the point itself. In Chapter 6 we shall give many examples of useful local operations on pictures, e.g., smoothing and sharpening operations.

EXERCISE 2. Write out the proof that a local operation is position-invariant.

One sometimes wants to consider operations ϕ that have natural definitions for particular classes of functions but that are not defined on all of $\mathscr{S}$. Suppose that the class of functions in question is "closed under translation"; in other words, if f is in the class, so is $T_{u,v}(f)$ for all u, v. (This is true, e.g., for the class of all integrable functions, the class of all continuous functions, the class of all picture functions, the class D_n of n-by-n digital picture functions for any given n, etc.) In such a case we can simply define ϕ to be, say, the identity operation on the rest of $\mathscr{S}$; readily, the resulting extended operation is still position-invariant. The following are two useful types of operations that have natural definitions for D_n; operations of these types will also be studied in Chapter 6.

d. Digital Point Operations

Let $\phi((a_{ij})) = (h(a_{ij}))$—the matrix whose (i, j) element is $h(a_{ij})$—where h is a nonnegative, real-valued function of one real variable. From the digital picture standpoint, ϕ can be thought of as a "point" operation, since it involves only a single matrix element.

e. Digital Local Operations

Let

$$\phi((a_{ij})) = (H(a_{i-1,\,j-1}, a_{i-1,\,j}, a_{i-1,\,j+1},$$
$$a_{i,\,j-1}, a_{ij}, a_{i,\,j+1}, a_{i+1,\,j-1},$$
$$a_{i+1,\,j}, a_{i+1,\,j+1}))$$

where H is a nonnegative, real-valued function of nine real variables, and a_{rs} is understood to be zero unless $1 \le r, s \le n$. From the digital picture standpoint, this can be regarded as a local operation, since it involves only the immediate "neighbors" of each matrix element. One can, of course, also define such operations using larger matrix "neighborhoods."

37

4.2. Position-Invariant Linear Operations

The operation ϕ is called *linear* (or sometimes *linear homogeneous*) if

$$\phi(af + bg) = a\phi(f) + b\phi(g)$$

for all f, g in $\mathscr{S}$ and all real a, b.

EXERCISE 1. Prove that (a) any geometrical operation (see Exercise 1 in Section 4.1) is linear; (b) a point operation is linear if the function h is of the form $h(z) = cz$, for some real number c. ★ Is the converse true?

Let g_0 be the n-by-n digital picture function defined by the matrix (c_{ij}), where $c_{11} = 1$ and $c_{ij} = 0$ for all other i, j. Then for any n-by-n digital picture function f, defined by the matrix (a_{ij}), we evidently have

$$f = \sum_{1 \le i, j \le n} a_{ij} T_{i-1, j-1}(g_0)$$

where $T_{i-1, j-1}$ is the translation required to take the subsquare S_{11} into the subsquare S_{ij}. Clearly, we can replace the limits of summation by $-\infty$ to ∞, since by definition, $a_{ij} = 0$, except for $1 \le i, j \le n$.

Let ϕ be a position-invariant linear operation; then we have

$$\phi(f) = \sum_{i, j = -\infty}^{\infty} a_{ij} \phi(T_{i-1, j-1}(g_0))$$

$$= \sum_{i, j = -\infty}^{\infty} a_{ij} T_{i-1, j-1}(\phi(g_0))$$

Thus the effect of ϕ on any digital picture function is completely determined by specifying its effect on g_0. Moreover, for all i, j we have $a_{ij} = f(i-1, j-1)$, so that if we denote $\phi(g_0)$ by g_ϕ, we have

$$[\phi(f)](x, y) = \sum_{i, j = -\infty}^{\infty} g_\phi(x - (i-1), y - (j-1)) f(i-1, j-1)$$

$$= \sum_{i, j = -\infty}^{\infty} g_\phi(x - i, y - j) f(i, j) \qquad (1)$$

EXERCISE 2. Verify that, if g_ϕ in (1) is an m-by-m digital picture function, then $\phi(f)$ is an $(n + m - 1)$-by-$(n + m - 1)$ digital picture function.

When working with continuous picture functions, it is convenient to assume that the continuous analog of (1) holds:

$$[\phi(f)](x, y) = \int_{-\infty}^{\infty} \int_{-\infty}^{\infty} g_\phi(x - u, y - v)f(u, v) \, du \, dv \qquad (2)$$

We shall assume from now on that any position-invariant linear operation is defined by an expression of the form (2).

> The proof of (2) is not mathematically trivial. We can regard a continuous picture function f as the limit of a sequence of n-by-n digital picture functions with larger and larger n's, but there is no guarantee that the corresponding sequence of $\phi(f)$'s converges.

Note that, conversely, if ϕ is the operation defined by (2), it is readily position-invariant and linear; thus (2) [and in the digital case, (1)] can be used to define classes of position-invariant linear operations. For example, in (2), let $g_\phi(u, v) = 0$ outside a neighborhood N of $(0, 0)$; then $g_\phi(x - u, y - v) = 0$ outside the corresponding (translated) neighborhood of (x, y), so that $[\phi(f)](x, y)$ depends only on the values of f in this neighborhood, making ϕ a *local linear operation*.

> To define a point operation in this way, we would have to assume that g_ϕ is of the form $c\delta$, where c is a constant and δ is a "delta function," i.e., a function such that
>
> $$\int_{-\infty}^{\infty} \int_{-\infty}^{\infty} \delta(x - u, y - v)f(u, v) \, du \, dv = f(x, y)$$
>
> for all x, y.

EXERCISE 3. Let $P = (p_{ij})$ and $Q = (q_{ij})$ be n-by-n matrices in which the elements on any line parallel to the main diagonal are all equal; in particular suppose that $p_{ij} = q_{ij} = 0$ except when $j = i - 1$, i or $i + 1$. Verify that the operation ϕ defined by $\phi(A) = PAQ$ [where $A = (a_{ij})$ is any n-by-n matrix] is a digital local operation of the type defined at the end of Section 4.1, and that this operation is linear. [On this method of defining linear local operations on digital pictures, see W. D. Fryer and G. E. Richmond, Two-dimensional spatial filtering and computers, *Proc. Nat. Electron. Confer.* **18**, 529–535 (1962); W. R. Tobler, Of maps and matrices, *J. Regional Sci.* **7**, 275–280 (1967).]

In the remainder of this section, we introduce some useful terminology and notation. The right member of (2) is called the *convolution* of f and g_ϕ, and is denoted by $f * g_\phi$. [Thus (2) can be restated in words as: Any position-invariant linear operation ϕ is a convolution operation—i.e., there exists some g (which we have denoted by g_ϕ) such that $\phi(f) = f * g$ for all f.] Note that by letting $x - u = u'$ and $y - v = v'$, we obtain

$$g * f = \iint g(u, v) f(x - u, y - v) \, du \, dv$$
$$= \iint g(x - u', y - v') f(u', v') \, du' dv' = f * g.$$

Let $\bar{g}$ denote the function obtained from g by replacing its arguments by their negatives, i.e., $\bar{g}(u, v) = g(-u, -v)$ for all u, v. The convolution $f * \bar{g}$ is called the *cross correlation* of f and g; we shall denote it by $f \otimes g$. Thus $f \otimes g = \iint g(u - x, v - y) f(u, v) \, du \, dv$; if we put $u' = u - x$, and $v' = v - y$, this becomes $\iint g(u', v') f(u' + x, v' + y) \, du' \, dv'$, a form that is more commonly used. Readily, we have $\overline{f * g} = \bar{f} * \bar{g}$, so that $g \otimes f = \overline{f \otimes g}$.

The cross correlation of f with itself, $f \otimes f$, is called the *autocorrelation* of f. Note that

$$[(T_{a,b}(f)) \otimes (T_{a,b}(f))](x, y) = \iint f(u - a, v - b) f(u - a + x, v - b + y) \, du \, dv$$
$$= \iint f(u - a, v - b) f(u - a + x, v - b + y) \, d(u - a) \, d(v - b)$$
$$= [f \otimes f](x, y)$$

so that the autocorrelation remains unchanged if f is translated. (The same is readily true for the "autoconvolution" of f.) Note also that $\overline{f \otimes f} = f \otimes f$, so that the autocorrelation is symmetrical about the origin.

4.3. Fourier Transforms

In this section we review some basic facts about Fourier transforms and indicate how they can be applied to the study of position-invariant linear operations.

By the *Fourier transform* of $f(x, y)$ is meant

$$F(w_x, w_y) = \int_{-\infty}^{\infty} \int_{-\infty}^{\infty} e^{2\pi j(w_x x + w_y y)} f(x, y) \, dx \, dy$$

where j denotes $\sqrt{-1}$. By the *inverse Fourier transform* of $F(w_x, w_y)$ is meant the complex conjugate of its Fourier transform, i.e.,

$$\int_{-\infty}^{\infty} \int_{-\infty}^{\infty} e^{-2\pi j(w_x x + w_y y)} F(w_x, w_y) \, dw_x \, dw_y$$

It is well known that this function is the same as the original $f(x, y)$ (this is the *invertibility* property of the Fourier transform), provided that f is sufficiently well-behaved.

The Fourier transform $F(w_x, w_y)$ is a complex function; since $e^{jz} = \cos z + j \sin z$, its real part and imaginary part are, respectively,

$$C(w_x, w_y) = \int_{-\infty}^{\infty} \int_{-\infty}^{\infty} \cos[2\pi(w_x x + w_y y)] f(x, y) \, dx \, dy$$

and

$$S(w_x, w_y) = \int_{-\infty}^{\infty} \int_{-\infty}^{\infty} \sin[2\pi(w_x x + w_y y)] f(x, y) \, dx \, dy$$

These are sometimes called the *cosine Fourier transform* and *sine Fourier transform* of f. The square of the modulus of $F(w_x, w_y)$—in other words, the product of $F(w_x, w_y)$ with its complex conjugate—is called the *power spectrum* (or sometimes, in optics, the *Wiener spectrum*) of f.

The analogous definitions in one dimension are

$$F(w_t) = \int_{-\infty}^{\infty} e^{2\pi j w_t t} f(t) \, dt$$

$$f(t) = \int_{-\infty}^{\infty} e^{-2\pi j w_t t} F(w_t) \, dw_t$$

$$C(w_t) = \int_{-\infty}^{\infty} \cos(2\pi w_t t) f(t) \, dt$$

$$S(w_t) = \int_{-\infty}^{\infty} \sin(2\pi w_t t) f(t) \, dt$$

As a simple illustration of the Fourier transform in one dimension, let $f(t) = 1$ for $-1 \le t \le 1$, $f(t) = 0$ elsewhere; then we have

$$F(w_t) = \int_{-1}^{1} e^{2\pi j w_t t} \, dt = e^{2\pi j w_t t}/2\pi j w_t \big|_{-1}^{1}$$

$$= (e^{2\pi j w_t} - e^{-2\pi j w_t})/2\pi j w_t = \sin(2\pi w_t)/\pi w_t$$

EXERCISE 1. Compute the Fourier transform and power spectrum of the function

$$f(x, y) = k \quad \text{if} \quad a \le x \le b, c \le y \le d$$
$$0 \quad \text{otherwise}$$

Taking the Fourier transform of a function is evidently a linear operation (defined on the set of complex-valued functions of two real variables), but it is not position-invariant. In fact if f is translated by $T_{r,s}$, the Fourier transform of the translated function is

$$\int_{-\infty}^{\infty} \int_{-\infty}^{\infty} e^{2\pi j(w_x x + w_y y)} f(x - r, y - s) \, dx \, dy$$

Letting $x' = x - r$ and $y' = y - s$, this becomes

$$\int_{-\infty}^{\infty} \int_{-\infty}^{\infty} e^{2\pi j[w_x(x'+r) + w_y(y'+s)]} f(x', y') \, dx' \, dy'$$

$$= e^{2\pi j(w_x r + w_y s)} \int_{-\infty}^{\infty} \int_{-\infty}^{\infty} e^{2\pi j(w_x x' + w_y y')} f(x', y') \, dx' \, dy'$$

$$= e^{2\pi j(w_x r + w_y s)} F(w_x, w_y)$$

Thus, translation of a function changes the phase of its Fourier transform, though it leaves the modulus unchanged.

In spite of the fact that the Fourier transform is not itself a position-invariant operation, it can be used to provide an alternative method of performing position-invariant linear operations. As indicated in Section 4.2, any such operation can be expressed as the convolution of some function with the given function. We shall now prove the *convolution theorem*, which states that *the convolution of two functions is equal to the inverse Fourier transform of the product of their Fourier transforms*. It follows that one can convolve two functions by taking their Fourier transforms, multiplying them, and taking the inverse Fourier transform of the result. With the recent development of efficient algorithms for computing the Fourier transform [1, 2], this procedure can even be faster than computing the convolution directly.

THEOREM. Let F and G be the Fourier transforms of f and g, respectively; then the inverse Fourier transform of FG is equal to the convolution $f*g$.

PROOF. Let H be the Fourier transform of $f*g$; it suffices to prove that $H = FG$. Now

$$H(w_x, w_y) = \iint e^{2\pi j(w_x x + w_y y)}\left[\iint f(x - u, y - v)g(u, v)\, du\, dv\right] dx\, dy$$

$$= \iint g(u, v)\left[\iint e^{2\pi j(w_x x + w_y y)} f(x - u, y - v)\, dx\, dy\right] du\, dv$$

But the bracketed integral in this last expression, as shown just above, is equal to $e^{2\pi j(w_x u + w_y v)} F(w_x, w_y)$. Hence

$$H(w_x, w_y) = \iint g(u, v)e^{2\pi j(w_x u + w_y v)}F(w_x, w_y)\, du\, dv$$

$$= F(w_x, w_y) \iint e^{2\pi j(w_x u + w_y v)}g(u, v)\, du\, dv$$

$$= F(w_x, w_y)G(w_x, w_y) \quad\blacksquare$$

"Convolution theorems" analogous to the one just proved also hold for other types of integral transforms, such as Laplace transforms, or their discrete analogs, Z-transforms. However, it is customary to use Fourier transforms rather than these other types in the study of position-invariant linear operations. One reason for this is that the Fourier transform can be computed optically in a very simple way, as we shall see in Section 5.4. Another reason is that since the Fourier transform is defined in terms of sinusoidal functions, it can be interpreted (compare the appendix to Chapter 3) as describing the *spatial frequencies* that are present in the original function.

Since we have just shown that the Fourier transform of $f*g$ is FG, it follows immediately that the Fourier transform of $f \otimes g = f*\bar{g}$ is $F\bar{G}$. But $\bar{G}(w_x, w_y) = \iint e^{2\pi j[(-w_x)x + (-w_y)y]}\, g(x, y)\, dx\, dy = \iint e^{-2\pi j(w_x x + w_y y)}\, g(x, y)\, dx\, dy$ is just the complex conjugate of $G(w_x, w_y)$. In particular, letting $g = f$, we have thus shown that the Fourier transform of the autocorrelation $f \otimes f$ is the product of F and its complex conjugate; in other words, it is the power spectrum of f.

EXERCISE 2. If f is symmetrical about the origin, i.e., if $f(-x, -y) = f(x, y)$ for all x, y, prove that F is real.

EXERCISE 3. Prove that the power spectrum is symmetrical about the origin.

43

REFERENCES

1. W. T. Cochran, J. W. Cooley, D. L. Favin, H. D. Helms, R. A. Kaenel, W. W. Lang, G. C. Maling, Jr., D. E. Nelson, C. M. Rader, and P. D. Welch, What is the fast Fourier transform?, *Proc. IEEE* **55**, 1664–1674 (October 1967).
2. J. W. Cooley, P. A. W. Lewis, and P. D. Welch, Historical notes on the fast Fourier transform, *ibid.* **55**, 1675–1677 (October 1967).

These papers are reprinted from the June 1967 issue of *IEEE Trans. Audio and Electroacoustics* (Special Issue on the Fast Fourier Transform).

4.4. Spread and Transfer Functions

a. *The Point Spread Function*

The function g_ϕ in (2) (Section 4.2) is called the *point spread function* of ϕ. In justification of this terminology, we recall that in the digital picture case, g was defined as the result of applying ϕ to the "one-point picture" g_0. In general ϕ will not take g_0 into a one-point picture; it can thus be thought of as "spreading" (or "blurring") the single nonzero value in g_0 over a region. When we assume that (2) holds, we are saying that any position-invariant linear operation is determined by specifying its point spread function.

In the continuous case too, (2) amounts to treating an arbitrary picture as the "sum" of a set of "one-point pictures." These one-point pictures are, of course, not physically realizable but can only be approximated. The point spread function is the two-dimensional analog of the *impulse response* in electronics; this is the output, as a function of time, that results from a "one-instant" input.

The integral of the point spread function of ϕ, taken from $-\infty$ to ∞, is a measure of the effect of ϕ on constant functions. In fact let $f(u, v) = c$ for all u, v; then $[\phi(f)](x, y) = c \iint g_\phi(x - u, y - v)\, du\, dv = c \iint g_\phi(x - u, y - v)\, d(x - u)\, d(y - v)$, which evidently does not depend on x and y. Let $\iint g_\phi(u, v)\, du\, dv = k_\phi$; then we have $\phi(c) = k_\phi c$ for all c. If $k_\phi > 1$, ϕ produces an over-all "intensification"; if $k_\phi < 1$, it produces an overall "attenuation."

b. *Other Spread Functions*

It is often convenient to describe ϕ in terms of its effect on some other simple type of input function rather than a one-point function. The case most commonly considered is that of a "one-line" function that is zero except at the points of a straight line, along which it has value 1. The result of applying ϕ to such a function is called a *line spread function* of ϕ. Another important case is that of a function which is 0 on one side of a line, and 1 on the other side; in this case the result of applying ϕ is called an *edge spread function* of ϕ. (If ϕ is not "isotropic," these functions will, in general, not be "orientation-invariant," but will depend on the slope of the line that is used.)

To see the relationship between the point and line spread functions, let h_0 be the one-line n-by-n digital picture function defined by the matrix (b_{ij}), in which b_{1j} is 1, while every other b_{ij} is 0. Evidently we have (where the notation is as in Section 4.2) $h_0 = \sum_{j=0}^{n-1} T_{0,j}(g_0)$. If we denote $\phi(h_0)$ by h_ϕ, we thus have

$$h_\phi(x, y) = \sum_{j=0}^{n-1} g_\phi(x, y - j)$$

Analogously, in the continuous case, we shall assume that

$$h_\phi(x, y) = \int_{-\infty}^{\infty} g_\phi(x, y - v)\, dv = \int_{-\infty}^{\infty} g_\phi(x, y - v)\, d(y - v)$$

In words: Any line spread function is obtained by integrating the point spread function in the direction parallel to the line. Note that $h_\phi(x, y)$ is independent of y, so that we can denote it by $h_\phi(x)$.

★EXERCISE 1. If ϕ is isotropic, can its point spread function be expressed in terms of its line spread function?

★EXERCISE 2. What is the relationship between the edge spread function and the line spread function?

c. *The Modulation Transfer Function*

Still another way of describing ϕ, in the continuous case, is by its effect on a sinusoidal input function, say $a + b \cos(2\pi wx)$. Now ϕ takes this function into $\iint g_\phi(x - u, y - v)[a + b \cos(2\pi wu)]\, du\, dv = k_\phi a + b \int h_\phi(x - u) \cos(2\pi wu)\, du$, since, as seen earlier in this section, we have $\iint g_\phi\, du\, dv = k_\phi$ and $\int g_\phi\, dv = h_\phi$. To evaluate the remaining integral, let $z = x - u$; then

45

$du = -dz$, but this sign change is cancelled by the fact that the limits of integration are interchanged, so that we have

$$\int h_\phi(x - u) \cos{(2\pi wu)}\, du = \int h_\phi(z) \cos{(2\pi w)}(x - z)\, dz$$
$$= \cos{(2\pi wx)} \int h_\phi(z) \cos{(2\pi wz)}\, dz$$
$$+ \sin{(2\pi wx)} \int h_\phi(z) \sin{(2\pi wz)}\, dz$$
$$= \cos{(2\pi wx)}\, C_\phi(w) + \sin{(2\pi wx)}\, S_\phi(w)$$

where $C_\phi(w)$ and $S_\phi(w)$ are the one-dimensional cosine and sine Fourier transforms of the line spread function $h_\phi(z)$. Let $M_\phi(w) = (C_\phi(w)^2 + S_\phi(w)^2)^{1/2}$ and $P_\phi(w) = \tan^{-1}{[S_\phi(w)/C_\phi(w)]}$; in other words, $M_\phi(w)$ is the modulus and $P_\phi(w)$ the phase of the Fourier transform of $h_\phi(z)$. Then the output function can be written as

$$k_\phi a + bM_\phi(w) \cos{(2\pi wx - P_\phi(w))}$$

In other words, this function is still sinusoidal and has the same period as $a + b \cos{(2\pi wx)}$ but different modulus and phase. $M_\phi(w)$ is called a *modulation transfer function*, and $P_\phi(w)$ a *phase transfer function*, of ϕ. If ϕ is not isotropic, these functions will, of course, depend on the orientation of the input sinusoid.

> The modulation transfer function corresponds to the *frequency response* in electronics. It can be thought of as describing how ϕ attenuates a sinusoidal input as a function of the spatial frequency of the input.

REFERENCES

1. R. L. Lamberts, Application of sine-wave techniques to image-forming systems, *J. Soc. Motion Picture Television Engrs.* **71**, 635–640 (September 1962).
2. F. D. Smith, Optical image evaluation and the transfer function, *Appl. Opt.* **2**, 335–350 (April 1963).
3. G. C. Higgins, Methods for engineering photographic systems, *ibid.* **3**, 1–10 (January 1964).
4. E. H. Linfoot, "Fourier Methods in Optical Image Evaluation." Focal Press, New York, 1964.
5. L. Ronchi and F. L. Van Nes, Contrast transfer in the eye as a function of spatial frequency: a literature survey, *Atti Fond. G. Ronchi* **21**, 218–234 (March-April 1966).

CHAPTER 5

Position-Invariant Operations on Pictures: 2, Implementations

5.1. Digital Implementations

It is a straightforward matter to "convolve" two digital pictures, using a digital computer to perform the required multiplications and additions. However, the number of multiplications (not counting those in which one factor must be zero) is readily m^2n^2, which grows very rapidly with m and n. Conventional digitial computers are basically *sequential*; they can perform only one (or, at most, a few) arithmetical operation(s) at a time. If it were possible to perform many identical arithmetical operations "in parallel" (i.e., simultaneously), great savings could be realized in the processing time required to convolve a pair of digital pictures. For this purpose, one could use a "parallel" computer [1–8] having many processing units (e.g., ILLIAC IV has 256) that operate under central control.

A more specifically picture-oriented approach to parallel computation involves special-purpose digital hardware that can perform operations simultaneously on each element of an array of numbers (i.e., a digital picture) ([9–14]; see also [15, 16]). If one could simultaneously shift an entire array in any of the four principal directions, and simultaneously add or multiply two arrays elementwise, one could convolve digital pictures very rapidly. In fact, for an m-by-m and an n-by-n picture, $(m + n - 1)^2$ shifts and multiplications (and about the same number of additions) would be required, in contrast to the m^2n^2 multiplications (and nearly as many additions) required by the sequential method. The ILLIAC III computer can process 36-by-36-element arrays in this parallel fashion.

Even on a conventional (sequential) digital computer, it is usually possible to perform simple logical and shifting operations simultaneously on each binary digit of a "word." This implies a potential saving in computation time by a factor equal to the word length, typically 32 or 36. Since arithmetical operations can be regarded as combinations of logical operations, much of this saving can be achieved for them as well, particularly if numbers having only a few binary digits (e.g., pictures having only a few gray levels) are involved. Several computer "languages" for picture processing have been developed ([17–19]; compare [20]) that take advantage of this approach.

REFERENCES

1. D. L. Slotnick, W. C. Borck, and R. C. McReynolds, The SOLOMON computer, *FJCC* pp. 97–107 (December 1962).
2. J. Gregory and R. McReynolds, The SOLOMON computer, *IEEE Trans. Electronic Computers* **EC-12**, 774–781 (December 1963).
3. D. N. Senzig and R. V. Smith, Computer organization for array processing, *FJCC* pp. 117–128 (November 1965).
4. J. C. Murtha, Highly parallel information processing systems, *Advances Comput.* **7**, 1–116 (1966).
5. M. Lehman, A survey of problems and preliminary results concerning parallel processing and parallel processors, *Proc. IEEE* **54**, 1889–1901 (December 1966).
6. R. H. Fuller, Associative parallel processing, *SJCC* pp. 471–475 (April 1967).
7. G. H. Barnes, R. M. Brown, M. Kato, D. J. Kuck, D. L. Slotnick, and R. A. Stokes, The ILLIAC IV computer, *IEEE Trans. Computers* **C-17**, 746–757 (August 1968).
8. D. J. Kuck, ILLIAC IV software and application programming, *ibid.* **C-17**, 758–770 (August 1968).
9. S. H. Unger, A computer oriented toward spatial problems, *Proc. IRE* **46**, 1744–1750 (October 1958).
10. S. H. Unger, Pattern detection and recognition, *ibid.* **47**, 1737–1752 (October 1959).
11. L. A. Kamentsky, Pattern and character recognition systems—picture processing by nets of neuron-like elements, *WJCC* pp. 304–309 (March 1959).
12. H. von Foerster, Circuitry of clues to Platonic ideation, "Aspects of the Theory of Artificial Intelligence: Proceedings, International Symposium on Biosimulation, 1st, Locarno, 1960" (C. A. Muses, ed.), pp. 43–81. Plenum Press, New York, 1962.
13. L. A. Edelstein, "Picture logic" for "Bacchus," a fourth-generation computer, *Comput. J.* **6**, 144–153 (July 1963).
14. B. H. McCormick, The Illinois pattern recognition computer—ILLIAC III, *IEEE Trans. Electronic Computers* **EC-12**, 791–813 (December 1963).
15. S. S. Yau and C. C. Yang, Pattern recognition using an associative memory, *ibid.* **EC-15**, 944–947 (December 1966).
16. M. C. Pease, An adaptation of the Fast Fourier Transform for parallel processing, *J. ACM* **15**, 252–264 (April 1968).
17. R. Narasimhan, Labeling schemata and syntactic descriptions of pictures, *Information and Control* **7**, 151–179 (July 1964).

18. R. Narasimhan, Syntax-directed interpretation of classes of pictures, *Comm. ACM* **9**, 166–173 (March 1966).
19. J. L. Pfaltz, J. W. Snively, Jr., and A. Rosenfeld, Local and global picture processing by computer, PPR, pp. 353–371.
20. G. A. Moore, Automatic scanning and computer processes for the quantitative analysis of micrographs and equivalent subjects, *ibid.*, pp. 275–326.

5.2. Electro-Optical Implementations

If digital circuitry is used to perform operations in parallel on large arrays of numbers, a large network of individual components, or the equivalent, is required. There exist other electronic methods of performing certain types of operations—in particular, position-invariant linear operations—in parallel, with the picture represented by an electronic analog (e.g., a pattern of voltages or charges) that is created directly from optical input. Two such methods are described in this section.

a. *EL-PC Arrays*†

Photoconductive (PC) devices have the property that their electrical resistance changes when they are illuminated. It is possible to deposit a layer of PC material on a surface in such a way as to create an array of small electrical circuits, each containing a small PC "element." A picture projected onto such an array is converted into a pattern of currents representing a digitized version of the picture. Moreover, it is possible to connect the array to an electroluminescent (EL) screen in such a way that the screen brightness at each point is, say, proportional to the voltage across the corresponding element of the array; thus the picture can be redisplayed.

Suppose that a screen and an array are made into a "sandwich," so that the light emitted by the screen falls on the array, while the array is connected to the screen as just described. Then a picture displayed on the screen activates the array, which in turn can (with amplification as necessary) maintain the picture on the screen. Thus, an EL-PC sandwich can be used to store a picture.

If a new picture is optically imaged on the array, it becomes added to the display on the screen; thus, addition of pictures is easy. [Note also that the voltages across the elements of the array can be electrically inverted, which

† See [1, 2].

(with the addition of a suitable constant positive voltage) has the effect of turning the displayed picture into a "negative"; thus, subtraction as well as addition can be performed.] To multiply a picture by a positive or negative constant, one can simply multiply (and invert) all the voltages electrically. By adding up displaced copies of a picture, each multiplied by a suitable constant, one can obtain arbitrary expressions of the form

$$\sum a_i f(x + u_i, y + v_i)$$

In other words, one can perform arbitrary position-invariant linear operations on a given picture f. A variety of nonlinear operations can also be performed by operating nonlinearly on the voltages.

b. *Image Tubes*†

Photoemissive surfaces emit electrons when they are illuminated; the number of electrons emitted from a point depends on the intensity of the light falling on that point. When subjected to a suitable electric field, these electrons can be made to travel along parallel paths until they are deposited on a grid, which thus acquires a pattern of charges corresponding to the input pattern of light intensities. In this way a picture imaged on the surface can be stored on the grid, and pictures can be added to one another. (To turn a picture into a negative, one can increase the electric field strength to the point where each electron arriving at the grid causes more than one "secondary" electron to be emitted. Thus, a high rate of emission at a point of the photoemissive surface results in a *reduction* in the charge at the corresponding point of the grid.) Multiplication by a constant is also easily accomplished by changing the field strength; and a picture can be displaced ("deflected") by adding a suitable sidewise component to the field. (Note that this method of displacement requires no moving parts, and can be performed very rapidly.) Thus, here again, arbitrary position-invariant linear operations can be very easily performed on a given picture.

REFERENCES

1. H. O. Hook and H. Weinstein, Image processing with optical panels, *Electronics* **34**, 35–39 (December 21, 1962).
2. T. E. Bray, Considerations in optoelectronic logic and memory arrays, OPI, pp. 216–232.

† See [3–6]; also [7, 8].

3. J. K. Hawkins and C. J. Munsey, An adaptive system with direct optical input, *Proc. IEEE* **55**, 1084–1085 (June 1967).
4. J. K. Hawkins and C. J. Munsey, Image processing by electron-optical techniques, *J. Opt. Soc. Amer.* **57**, 914–918 (July 1967).
5. J. K. Hawkins and C. J. Munsey, Parallel logic with charge storage techniques, *IEEE Trans. Electronic Computers* **EC-16**, 507–508 (August 1967).
6. J. K. Hawkins, Parallel electro-optical picture processing, PPR, pp. 373–385.
7. J. M. Abraham, C. E. Catchpole, and G. W. Goodrich, Image processing with multi-aperture image dissector, *J. Soc. Photo-Opt. Instr. Engrs.* **6**, 93–96 (February-March 1968). (Scans the picture with a 3-by-3 array of "apertures," and performs local operations on the picture by operating on the resulting nine signals electronically.)
8. J. K. Russell, A visual image processor, *IEEE Trans. Computers* **C–17**, 635–639 (July 1968). (Stores copies of the picture in two storage tubes; under electronic control, performs arbitrary operations on pairs of individual points and stores the results in a third tube.)

5.3. Optical Implementations: Methods Not Requiring Coherent Light

Position-invariant linear operations on pictures can be implemented in especially simple ways by optical means. Although in this book we are primarily concerned with picture processing by digital computer, the growing interest in optical and hybrid optical-digital computation makes it desirable to review such methods as well.

In optical picture processing the pictures are usually assumed to be in the form of *transparencies*; here, the picture function $f(x, y)$ represents the fraction of the light incident on the point (x, y) that is transmitted through the transparency. Note that transmittance is always nonnegative; we will discuss how to perform subtraction and to represent functions that may be negative-valued at the end of this section.

A picture that has been stored in a computer memory (or in some other electronic form) can be converted into a transparency by using a cathode ray tube to "write" it on a piece of film; here, it would normally be preferable to use an erasable, reusable medium requiring no developing, such as photochromic material, rather than conventional photographic film. (On other schemes for converting a picture from electronic to optical form, see [1, 2].) Conversely, a picture that has been processed optically can be converted to an electrical signal, using a television camera or similar scanning device; for examples of systems that do this, see [3–6].

To multiply f and g optically, we can simply superimpose their transparencies, since the fraction of light transmitted through a point of the superimposed transparencies is just the product of the fractions transmitted through the corresponding points of the individual transparencies. Similarly, to add f and g, we can superimpose images of their transparencies; the amount of light at each point of the composite image is the sum of the amounts in the individual images, which in turn are proportional to the amounts transmitted by the transparencies at the corresponding points. Thus, to obtain a transparency of fg, we can photographically copy f and g in contact; while to obtain a transparency of $f + g$, we can make a double exposure, first of f and then of g.

In the following paragraphs we describe a number of methods of cross correlating (or equivalently, convolving†) two picture functions by purely optical means. One could, of course, perform cross correlation by simply shifting one transparency relative to the other, and cumulatively adding the resulting sequence of products; but this would require moving parts and would be very time consuming. As we shall now see, optical cross correlation can be performed "instantaneously" and without the need for moving parts [7–15].

a. The Lensless Correlator

An extremely simple method of optically cross correlating two functions is shown in Figure 5.1; for simplicity, we describe the method for functions of a single variable. Let f and g be zero outside intervals of length $2r$ and $2s$, respectively. As indicated in the figure, the transparency representing g is made

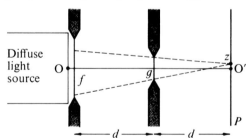

Figure 5.1. Lensless correlator.

† Evidently, one can convolve two functions by simply "reversing" one of them (i.e., rotating it through 180°) and cross correlating.

to half scale, so that its transmittance at distance y from the axis OO′ is $g(2y)$. [This choice of scale factor corresponds to the use of equal spacing d between f and g and between g and P; more generally, if the spacings are d_1 and d_2, respectively, the scale of the g transparency should be $d_2/(d_1 + d_2)$ times that of the f transparency.]

There are light rays from the light source passing through each point of f in all directions, and some of these pass through g. A ray that reaches the plane P at the point z must have passed through g, say, at the point y, which means that it comes from the point $2y - z$ on f. Thus the total amount of light at z is given by $\int_{-s/2}^{s/2} g(2y)f(2y - z)\, dy$. Let $w = 2y$, and note that since $g(w) = 0$ for $|w| > s$, we can replace the interval of integration by $(-\infty, \infty)$, so that the integral becomes $\frac{1}{2}\int_{-\infty}^{\infty} f(w - z)\, g(w)\, dw$. The amount of light reaching P, as a function of z, is thus proportional to the cross correlation of f and g.

b. One-Lens Correlators

The following elementary facts about (ideal) lenses will be used in this section:

Let L be a convex spherical lens (i.e., a lens whose two surfaces are spherical caps); the line joining the centers of the spheres is called the *optical axis* of L. If a beam of parallel light rays strikes L, it is *focused* to a single point. For every such beam, the *focal point* always lies in the same plane, perpendicular to the optical axis; this plane is called the *focal plane* of L. The position of the focal point in the focal plane depends on the orientation of the beam relative to the optical axis; specifically, it is the point at which the line through the center of L, parallel to the beam, intersects the focal plane. The distance from L (the thickness of which we shall ignore) to the focal plane is called the *focal length* of L; we shall denote it by ℓ (a more common notation is F, but we have been using F to denote the Fourier transform of the function f). Conversely, the light rays through any point at distance ℓ from L become a parallel beam after passing through L; the direction of this beam is the same as that of the line from the point through the center of L.

Finally, let (x, y) be any point in the plane perpendicular to the optical axis at distance u from L, where $u > \ell$. Then all light rays through (x, y) are focused to a single *image point* in an *image plane*,

53

perpendicular to the optical axis, at distance v on the opposite side of L, where u and v satisfy

$$\frac{1}{u} + \frac{1}{v} = \frac{1}{\ell}$$

Moreover, the position of this image point in the image plane is $(-vx/u, -vy/u)$.

Another optical cross-correlation scheme, in which both transparencies can be to the same scale, is shown in Figure 5.2. Here ℓ is the focal length of

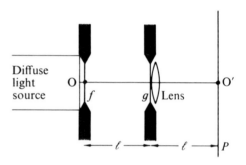

Figure 5.2. One-lens correlator.

the lens, so that any set of parallel light rays that strikes the lens is focused to a single point in the plane P. In particular consider the ray, through any point x of the f transparency, that makes given a angle θ with the axis OO′; this ray strikes the g transparency at the point $y = x + \ell \tan \theta$, and is focused at the point $z = \ell \tan \theta$ in P. The total amount of light striking P at this point is thus $\int_{-r}^{r} f(x)g(x + \ell \tan \theta)\,dx = \int_{-r}^{r} f(x)g(x + z)\,dx$, where again we can replace the interval of integration by $(-\infty, \infty)$ to obtain the cross correlation of g and f. (If the spacing between the two transparencies is not equal to ℓ, we still obtain the cross correlation in P, but at other than a 1 : 1 scale.)

An alternative one-lens correlator configuration, appropriate to picture functions given as transparencies at different scales, is shown in Figure 5.3. Here $1/u + 1/v = 1/\ell$, so that the lens focuses the rays emerging from each point of the light source onto a single point in the plane P. Consider the light rays originating at the point x of the source. These rays, after passing through the transparency f and the lens, form a beam that converges toward the point

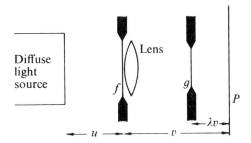

Figure 5.3. Alternative one-lens correlator.

$-vx/u$ in P. The brightness of a cross section of this beam is evidently described by the function f, except that the scale shrinks steadily as P is approached. Let the scale of g be λ times that of f, where $\lambda < 1$, and let g be at distance λv from P. The light ray from the point x of the source through the point y on f passes through the point $\lambda y - (1 - \lambda)vx/u$ on g, so that the total amount of light striking P at $-vx/u$ is $\int f(y)g(\lambda[y-((1 - \lambda)v/\lambda u)x])\,dy$, giving us a scaled cross correlation of g and f in P.

> The use of this last one-lens correlator configuration provides a simple means of converting the correlogram into an electrical signal for electronic processing. Specifically, we replace the diffuse light source with a cathode ray tube (or other type of flying–spot-scanning device), only one point of which is illuminated at a time. This implies that only one point of the correlogram is illuminated at a time, so that a photocell viewing the image plane will output a signal representing a scan of the correlogram.

c. *A One-Lens, One-Transparency Autocorrelator†*

To obtain the autocorrelation of a picture function optically, one can simply make two transparencies of it and use any of the cross-correlation schemes already described. One can also obtain the autocorrelation by using only a single transparency and employing the optical configuration shown in Figure 5.4. Here, $O_1O_2 + O_2O_3 = O_3O_2 + O_2O_4 = \ell$, the focal length of the lens, so that the light rays from any point x of the source, after reflection from the half-silvered mirror, emerge from the lens as a parallel family of rays in the

† See [16].

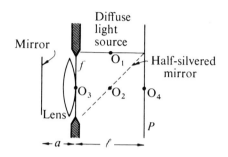

Figure 5.4. One-lens, one-transparency autocorrelator.

direction $\theta = \tan^{-1}(x/\ell)$. This family of rays strikes the mirror, and is reflected back through the transparency; evidently, the ray that passed through the transparency at point y is reflected back through point $y + 2a\tan\theta = y + 2ax/\ell$. Since the reflected family of rays is readily still parallel, though now in the direction $-\theta$, it is focused (after passing through the half-silvered mirror) to the point $z = \ell\tan(-\theta) = -x$ in the plane P. The total amount of light striking P at this point is thus $\int f(y)f(y + 2ax/\ell)\,dy$, giving a scaled autocorrelation of f.

> All of these schemes based on the use of diffuse light sources suffer from the defect that the families of parallel light rays emerging from the source at various angles are not equally bright; the larger an angle a ray makes with the perpendicular to the surface of the light source, the dimmer it is. In the configurations of Figures 5.2 and 5.4, this implies that the parts of the correlogram corresponding to large displacements are dimmer. In the configurations of Figures 5.1 and 5.3, on the other hand, even the rays reaching a single point of the "correlogram" are not equally bright, so that the total light incident on the point is represented only approximately by the integral shown; however, the approximation will be fairly good if the angles involved are small.

We now consider the question of how to operate optically on functions that are not necessarily nonnegative. Let g be such a function, and define the positive and negative parts of g by

$$g^+ = g \quad \text{if } g \geq 0, \qquad g^+ = 0 \quad \text{if } g < 0$$
$$g^- = -g \quad \text{if } g \leq 0, \qquad g^- = 0 \quad \text{if } g > 0$$

Thus g^+ and g^- are nonnegative, so that they can be realized as transparencies; while $g = g^+ - g^-$, so that, if we could subract two picture functions optically, we could obtain any given g. Moreover, for any f, we have $g \otimes f = g^+ \otimes f - g^- \otimes f$, so that any position-invariant linear operation can be performed on f by cross correlating two (nonnegative) picture functions with f and subtracting the results. In the following paragraphs we describe some methods of subtracting picture functions.

1. *Positive biasing.* Let c be the maximum value of the picture function g; then $c - g$ is nonnegative and so is realizable as a transparency (which is, in effect, a photographic negative of g). Thus, for any picture function f, we have $f + (c - g) = (f - g) + c$; in other words, we can subtract g from f ("up to a constant") by adding a "negative" of g to f. [More generally, let h be any function, and let c be the maximum value of h^-. Then $h + c = h^+ + (c - h^-)$ is nonnegative; in other words, we can represent any function as a transparency "up to a constant." Since $(h + c) \otimes f = h \otimes f + c \iint f$, we can thus perform any position-invariant linear operation on f up to a constant (where the constant now depends on f).] The chief objection to this approach is that the presence of the constant reduces the range of values that can be physically represented on a transparency. In particular if a transparency of c is almost completely transparent, it becomes difficult to represent values of $(f - g) + c$ that require even greater transmittance. This problem becomes particularly acute if one wants to perform a succession of position-invariant linear operations, each of which introduces an additional constant.

2. *Electronic subtraction.* One can subtract two picture functions by scanning them synchronously to obtain two electrical signals, which can be subtracted electronically. In particular suppose that g^+ and g^- are optically cross correlated with f, and the resulting correlograms are (synchronously) scanned by using flying-spot scanners in place of the diffuse light sources, as described earlier; then $g \otimes f$ can be obtained by electronic subtraction. In fact two separate optical correlators are not necessary; we can combine g^+ and g^- into a single transparency, using color- or polarization-separation techniques. Specifically, suppose that in the one-lens correlator configuration of Figure 5.3, we introduce a half-silvered mirror between the second transparency and the plane P, as shown in Figure 5.5; thus, half of the light is reflected from this mirror to the plane P'. Let H and V be sheets of vertically and horizontally polarizing material, respectively, and suppose that the transparency g is made out of vertically polarizing material at the points where $g^+ > 0$, and out of horizontally polarizing material at the points where

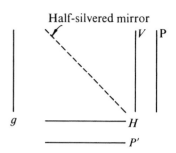

Figure 5.5. Separation technique for subtraction.

$g^- > 0$. Now, a vertical polarizer is transparent to light that has passed through another vertical polarizer, but is opaque to light that has passed through a horizontal polarizer, and vice versa. Hence, g, as viewed from the plane P, is opaque where $g^- > 0$, so that its transmittance is given by g^+, and we have the cross correlation $g^+ \otimes f$ in P; similarly, we have $g^- \otimes f$ in P'. If the light source is replaced by a flying spot, these correlograms will be scanned synchronously, and we can subtract them as required. A similar result is obtained if we make g out of pieces of color filters having disjoint spectral transmittances, rather than out of polarizing material; here, each material is opaque to the light that passes through the other, and we can use the same optical configuration with color filters replacing V and H.

The chief disadvantage of these methods is that they require g to be assembled from pieces of two different materials, which is impractical unless relatively few pieces are required. Another method involving polarization, which does not have this disadvantage, will be described in the next section.

3. *Photographic reversal effects* [17]. When long-wavelength light strikes exposed (but undeveloped) photographic film, the latent image on the film is "erased" to a degree proportional to the intensity of the light; this phenomenon is known as the *Herschel effect*. Suppose that film is exposed (using ordinary light) to a transparency of f, and simultaneously, or at any subsequent time prior to being developed, it is also exposed (using long-wavelength light) to a transparency of g. The resultant latent image then represents $af - bg$, wherever this is nonnegative [in other words, it represents $(af - bg)^+$] and where the constants a and b depend on the exposure times. Thus,

one can compute $(g \otimes f)^+$ by exposing film to $g^+ \otimes f$ in the output plane of an optical correlator using ordinary light, and then to $g^- \otimes f$, using long-wavelength light. (Here again, in principle, the two exposures can be made simultaneously by constructing g out of two types of material—each of which is opaque to one type of light and transparent to the other—and using a light source having output in both ranges.)

> Although this method, as well as the one that follows, yields only $(g \otimes f)^+$, this may be quite sufficient for many purposes. For example, if g is an "edge-detector" template (Section 6.5), it suffices to know the positive values of $g \otimes f$ in order to detect edges in f.

4. *Quenchable phosphors* [18]. There exist phosphors that fluoresce when they are illuminated by ultraviolet light, but whose fluorescence is "quenched" under infrared illumination. Thus, if such a phosphor is illuminated with ultraviolet light that has passed through a transparency of f, and also with infrared light that has passed through a transparency of g, it will fluoresce in a pattern that represents $(af - bg)^+$, where the constants a and b depend on the brightnesses of the light sources. It follows that one can compute $(g \otimes f)^+$ by optically superimposing, on a quenchable phosphor screen, the image planes containing $g^+ \otimes f$ and $g^- \otimes f$, using ultraviolet and infrared light, respectively. (Here too, one can use a single optical correlator with such a screen in its image plane and construct g out of two types of material; one of them opaque to ultraviolet, the other opaque to infrared.)

REFERENCES

1. A. S. Hoffman, Electrolytic cell for use as a real-time spatial filter, *J. Opt. Soc. Amer.* **56**, 828–829 (June 1966).
2. W. J. Poppelbaum, Adaptive on-line Fourier transform, PPR, pp. 387–394.
3. W. S. Holmes, T. R. Babcock, G. E. Richmond, L. A. Pownall, and G. C. Vorie, Optical-electronic spatial filtering for pattern recognition, OEOIP, pp. 199–207.
4. J. E. Rau, Real-time complex spatial modulation, *J. Opt. Soc. Amer.* **57**, 798–802 (June 1967).
5. J. W. Goodman and R. W. Lawrence, Digital image formation from electronically generated holograms, *Appl. Phys. Lett.* **11**, 77–79 (August 1, 1967).

6. R. M. Stock and J. J. Deener, A real-time input preprocessor for a pattern recognition computer, *Proc. IEEE Comput. Confer.* pp. 149–152 (September 1967).
7. D. McLachlan, Jr., The role of optics in applying correlation functions to pattern recognition, *J. Opt. Soc. Amer.* **52**, 454–459 (April 1962).
8. J. K. Hawkins and C. J. Munsey, A natural image computer, OPI, pp. 233–245.
9. J. K. Hawkins and C. J. Munsey, A parallel computer organization and mechanizations, *IEEE Trans. Electronic Computers* **EC-12**, 251–262 (June 1963).
10. J. K. Hawkins and C. J. Munsey, Automatic photo reading, *Photogrammetric Engrg.* **29**, 632–640 (July 1963).
11. J. K. Hawkins and C. J. Munsey, Eulogismographic nonlinear optical image processing for pattern recognition, *J. Opt. Soc. Amer.* **54**, 998–1003 (August 1964).
12. J. K. Hawkins, Photographic techniques for extracting image shapes, *Phot. Sci. Engrg.* **8**, 329–335 (November-December 1964).
13. P. L. Jackson, Correlation function spatial filtering with incoherent light, *Appl. Opt.* **6**, 1272–1273 (July 1967).
14. M. De and A. W. Lohmann, Signal detection by correlation of Fresnel diffraction patterns, *ibid.* **6**, 2171–2175 (December 1967).
15. E. L. Green, Diffraction in lensless correlation, *ibid.* **7**, 1237–1239 (June 1968).
16. L. S. G. Kovasznay and A. Arman, Optical autocorrelation measurement of two-dimensional random patterns, *Rev. Sci. Instr.* **28**, 793–797 (October 1957).
17. D. H. Kelly, Image processing experiments, *J. Opt. Soc. Amer.* **51**, 1095–1101 (October 1961).
18. E. A. Trabka and P. G. Roetling, Image transformations for pattern recognition using incoherent illumination and bipolar aperture masks, *ibid.* **54**, 1242–1252 (October 1964).

GENERAL REFERENCES

1. B. J. Howell, Optical analog computers, *J. Opt. Soc. Amer.* **49**, 1012–1021 (October 1959).
2. N. F. Barber, "Experimental Correlograms and Fourier Transforms." Macmillan, New York, 1961.
3. A. Vander Lugt, A review of optical data-processing techniques, *Optica Acta* **15**, 1–33 (1968).

5.4. Optical Implementations: Methods Requiring Coherent Light

For this section, we need some basic facts about the wave nature of light. A ray of light can be regarded as a sinusoidal wave disturbance, say of wavelength λ where λ depends on the color of the light. If the waves travel at velocity c, then their frequency (number of waves per second) is c/λ. Thus, the wave can be represented at any point by an expression of the form $A\, e^{j(2\pi ct/\lambda + \varphi)}$, where it can be shown that the intensity of the light is proportional to A^2. Note that if we move a distance z along the ray, the phase changes by the amount $2\pi z/\lambda$.

When a light ray passes through an object, both its modulus and phase will, in general, be changed, so that it becomes, say,

$$KA\, e^{j(2\pi ct/\lambda + \varphi + \psi)}$$

Evidently, if a parallel beam of light passes through an object of constant thickness, each ray will be affected identically; thus, the phase of each ray after passing through the object differs by a constant from its phase just before entering the object, and this constant is the same for each ray. It can also be shown that if a parallel beam passes through a lens, and is focused to a point, the phase of each ray when it reaches the focal point differs by a constant (the same constant for each ray) from its phase when crossing any given plane perpendicular to the optical axis before entering the lens. (The fact that a ray that passes through the lens near its center must pass through a greater thickness of the lens than a ray that passes through the lens near its edge is exactly compensated by the fact that the ray near the center travels a shorter distance to reach the focal point than the ray near the edge.)

A parallel beam of light is called *coherent* if each ray in it, when crossing any plane perpendicular to the beam, has the same phase. By the remarks in the preceding paragraph, a coherent beam remains coherent after passing through an object of constant thickness; and if such a beam is focused to a point by a lens, each ray has the same phase when it arrives at the focal point.

Two rays of light (of the same wavelength) that have different phases can "interfere" with each other; in particular if the phases differ by π, the rays can cancel completely, since

$$A\, e^{j(2\pi ct/\lambda + \varphi + \pi)} = e^{j\pi} A\, e^{j(2\pi ct/\lambda + \varphi)}$$

where we recall that $e^{j\pi} = -1$. Interference prevents a beam of light from spreading in all directions; in fact one can think of each point of the cross section of the beam as a "point source" emitting spherical waves, but when the waves emitted by all the points are summed, it turns out that they cancel each other, except in the original direction of the beam. On the other hand, if parts of the beam are blocked, this self-interference can no longer take place in every direction, and the beam is (partially) *diffracted* into new directions. In particular suppose that a coherent beam passes through a "sinusoidal diffraction grating," i.e., a plate of constant thickness whose transmittance varies sinusoidally as a function of, say, x, for all y; then it can be shown that the light is diffracted in just two symmetrical directions, making an angle (with the original direction of the beam) that depends on the spacing of the grating lines and on the wavelength of the light.

a. *The Focal Plane Fourier Transform*

Let the transparency f in Figure 5.6 be illuminated by a coherent beam of light of wavelength λ, parallel to the optical axis; thus, each ray of the beam incident on the plane of f has the same modulus E_0 and phase φ_0. Let the

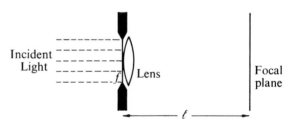

Incident Light   Lens   Focal plane

     ℓ

Figure 5.6. Focal plane Fourier transform.

ray passing through f at the point (x, y) be attenuated in modulus by the factor $f(x, y)$ and retarded in phase by $\varphi(x, y)$, so that the modulus and phase of the ray as it emerges from f are $f(x, y)E_0$ and $\varphi(x, y) + \varphi_0$, respectively.

On passing through f, the light is diffracted; let us consider that part of the light which is diffracted at a given angle, having direction cosines (with respect to the x and y axes) a_1 and a_2. This parallel family of light rays is focused by the lens to a single point in the image plane, whose coordinates w_x and w_y are proportional to a_1 and a_2—the factor of proportionality being ℓ/a_3, where $a_1{}^2 + a_2{}^2 + a_3{}^2 = 1$ and ℓ is the focal length of the lens. Let P be the plane through the center of f whose normal has direction cosines a_1 and a_2; then, the phase of the ray through (x, y) when it crosses P is $\varphi_0 +$

$\varphi(x, y) + 2\pi(a_1 x + a_2 y)/\lambda$. But as indicated at the beginning of the section, the phase of the ray through (x, y) when it arrives at (w_x, w_y) differs by a constant from its phase when crossing P. The sum of the rays at (w_x, w_y) is thus proportional to

$$\iint f(x, y) e^{j[\varphi(x, y) + 2\pi(a_1 x + a_2 y)/\lambda]} \, dx \, dy$$

where the second term in the brackets is equal to $2\pi a_3 (w_x + w_y)/\ell \lambda$, so that the integral becomes

$$\iint [f(x, y) e^{j\varphi(x, y)}] e^{2\pi a_3 j(w_x x + w_y y)/\ell \lambda} dx \, dy$$

Figure 5.7. Power spectrum of a circular aperture [$f(x, y) = 1$ for $0 \le (x^2 + y^2)^{1/2} \le 0.1$ mm, $f(x, y) = 0$ elsewhere] recorded in the focal plane of a lens.

If diffraction at large angles is assumed to be negligible, we may suppose that $a_3 \doteq 1$ is independent of (w_x, w_y), so that this becomes just the Fourier transform of the complex function $f(x, y) e^{j\varphi(x, y)}$, scaled by the factor $1/\ell\lambda$. (The light intensity in the focal plane is, thus, just the square of the modulus of this Fourier transform, i.e., the power spectrum of f. It is thus easy to make a transparency representing the power spectrum of f by simply putting a piece of photographic film in the focal plane. A simple example of a power spectrum recorded in this way, using an f that is transparent in a circle centered on the optical axis, and opaque elsewhere, is shown in Figure 5.7. The power spectra of two cloud-cover pictures, obtained in the same way, are shown in Figure 5.8.)

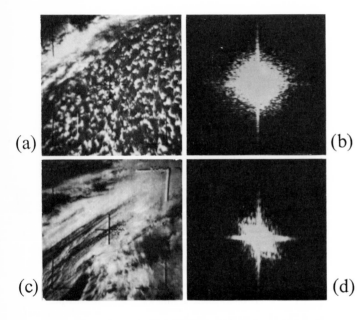

(a) (b) (c) (d)

Figure 5.8. Two TIROS cloud-cover pictures and their power spectra. If a picture contains much fine detail and many "edges," its spectrum extends relatively far from the origin, corresponding to relatively high spatial frequencies (a and b). If the edges in a picture have a marked directional bias, its spectrum is markedly nonisotropic (c and d).

b. *Application to Convolution*†

One can use the Fourier transforming configuration just described to perform position-invariant linear operations on f. In fact, to convolve f with g, we place a transparency of G (the Fourier transform of g, suitably scaled) in the focal plane. (How such a transparency can be made will be discussed

† See [1–9].

next.) Since the light incident on this plane is the Fourier transform of f, and passage through the transparency multiplies this by G, we now have the product FG of the Fourier transforms of f and g. In Figure 5.9, if lens L_2 is

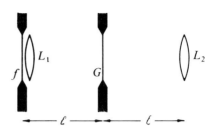

Figure 5.9. Use of a symmetrical optical system for complex spatial filtering.

identical to L_1, and its distance from the plane of G is also ℓ, then by symmetry, the relationship between the pattern of light emerging from G and that emerging from L_2 is the same as the relationship between the pattern of light entering G and that entering L_1. Thus the light pattern emerging from L_2 is the inverse Fourier transform of FG, i.e., the convolution of f and g.

c. Realization of the Fourier Transform as a Transparency

We have assumed in the preceding paragraph that G is the complex Fourier transform of g. As already remarked, it is easy in principle to create a transparency representing the power spectrum of a given function, but to incorporate phase information into this transparency is more difficult. In the following paragraphs we describe some of the possible ways of doing this.

1. *Relief* [10]. When light passes through a transparency, its phase is shifted by an amount proportional to the thickness of the transparency. Thus, if a transparency could be made in such a way that both its transmittance and its thickness varied arbitrarily from point to point, both the modulus and phase of a complex function could, in principle, be represented by it. In practice it is sometimes even sufficient to crudely approximate the desired phase information by using several discrete thicknesses.

2. *Polarization separation* [11]. Suppose that the Fourier transform G is real (this is true, e.g., in the important class of cases in which g is symmetric about the origin). Even if G is real, it need not be nonnegative; but we can now break it up into positive and negative parts, as in Section 5.3, and use an appropriate subtraction method. Since the light must be coherent, hence monochromatic, we cannot use methods involving color separation in a

65

single optical system; but we can use polarization separation methods. Indeed, the fact that the light is coherent allows us to use a special polarization technique, which requires only a single path. Let the transparency of G be made from pieces of polarizing material, as described in Section 5.3, and let the incoming light be polarized in the $+45°$ direction, while the outgoing light is passed through a polarizer at $-45°$. Then it can be shown that outgoing light rays that have passed through the G^+ and the G^- parts of the transparency will be polarized at $-45°$ but in opposite "senses"; and since they have the same phase, they will subtract from one another. We can now also make the transparency without having to cut out separate pieces for the G^+ and G^- parts by using a two-layer material known as Vectograph film (a Polaroid Corporation trade name). When a function is recorded on one layer of this film, its transmittance becomes variable to a degree which depends on the direction of polarization of the incident light; the layer remains completely transparent to light polarized in a certain direction. We can thus record G^+ on one layer and G^- on the other, with the first layer remaining completely transparent to horizontally polarized light and the second remaining completely transparent to vertically polarized light.

3. *Diffraction gratings* [12, 13]. When parts of a beam of coherent light are blocked, the beam is diffracted, and the modulus and phase of the diffracted light depend on the pattern of points at which the beam was blocked. By controlling this pattern, one can, in principle, realize any desired complex function not only as a real, but even as a binary, picture, i.e., a pattern of opaque points. Consider, as a simple example, the one-dimensional case in which the beam is blocked by a pattern of parallel opaque strips separated by transparent slits; this is a sort of generalized "diffraction grating." Specifically, let the cross-section of the beam be divided into strips of width δ; we want to put a transparent slit of width $\alpha_n \delta$, centered at distance β_n from the center of the nth strip, with α_n and β_n chosen so that we obtain the arbitrary output $A_n e^{j\varphi_n}$ from the input $A e^{jwx}$, which corresponds to a parallel coherent light beam incident on the grating at an angle. But, in fact, the output wave from the nth slit is

$$\int_{(n+\beta_n-\alpha_n/2)\delta}^{(n+\beta_n+\alpha_n/2)\delta} A e^{jwx} \, dx = (2A/w) e^{jw(n+\beta_n)\delta} \sin(\alpha_n w\delta/2)$$

so that we need only choose α_n such that $(2A/w)\sin(\alpha_n w\delta/2) = A_n$, and β_n such that $w(n + \beta_n)\delta = \varphi_n$.

4. *Modulation of a carrier pattern* [14–26]. If one does not actually need

a transparency representing the complex Fourier transform G of g, but only wants to convolve g with another function, one can use a transparency in which G is mixed with a "reference signal" in such a way that the convolution process separates it out. Suppose, in fact, that we form G optically in a focal plane, and also illuminate this plane with with a coherent, parallel light beam R incident on the plane at an angle, so that $R = |R|\, e^{2\pi j(aw_x + bw_y)}$, where $|R|$, a, and b are constants, and w_x and w_y are the coordinates in the plane. The resulting light intensity, which can be recorded on a transparency, is $|G + R|^2 = |G|^2 + |R|^2 + GR^* + RG^*$, where the asterisk denotes the complex conjugate. (Figure 5.10 shows such a recording of the Fourier

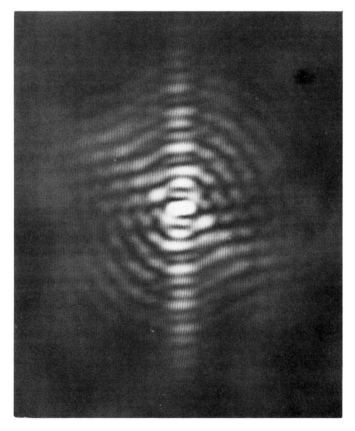

Figure 5.10. Fourier transform of the character "3," mixed with a reference signal.

transform of the character " 3.") If we now multiply by the Fourier transform F of f and take the inverse transform, we obtain

$$\iint F(|G|^2 + |R|^2)e^{-2\pi j(w_x x + w_y y)}\, dw_x\, dw_y$$

$$+ |R| \iint FG\, e^{-2\pi j[w_x(x+a)+w_y(y+b)]}\, dw_x\, dw_y$$

$$+ |R| \iint FG^* e^{-2\pi j[w_x(x-a)+w_y(y-b)]}\, dw_x\, dw_y$$

Here, the second and third terms are "displaced" from the first term in the (x, y) plane by the amounts $(-a, -b)$ and (a, b), respectively; thus, if each term is nearly zero outside a bounded region, we can choose (a, b) so that the terms are displayed separately in the (x, y) plane. The second term, except for its displacement and for the constant factor $|R|$, is then the desired convolution of f and g.

> Interference patterns from which a given picture can be "reconstructed" are used in *holography*. For references to the rapidly growing literature on holography, see [27]; for comprehensive treatments of the subject, see [28, 29]; compare [30].

REFERENCES

1. E. L. O'Neill, Spatial filtering in optics, *IRE Trans. Information Theory* **IT-2**, 56–65 (June 1956).
2. G. F. Aroyan, The technique of spatial filtering, *Proc. IRE* **47**, 1561–1568 (September 1959).
3. L. J. Cutrona, E. N. Leith, and L. J. Porcello, Filtering operations using coherent optics, *Proc. Nat. Electron. Confer.* pp. 262–275 (October 1959).
4. L. J. Cutrona, E. N. Leith, C. J. Palermo, and L. J. Porcello, Optical data processing and filtering systems, *IRE Trans. Information Theory* **IT-6**, 386–400 (June 1960).
5. A. Marechal, Optical filtering by double diffraction, OPI, pp. 20–30.
6. K. Preston, Jr., Use of the Fourier transformable properties of lenses for signal analysis, OEOIP, pp. 59–68.
7. G. Lansraux, Contributions of diffraction optics to optical information technology, *ibid.*, pp. 69–81.
8. L. J. Cutrona, Recent developments in coherent optical technology, *ibid.*, pp. 83–123.

9. E. N. Leith, A. Kozma, and J. Upatnieks, Coherent optical systems for data processing, spatial filtering, and wavefront reconstruction, *ibid.*, pp. 143–158.

10. H. M. Smith, Photographic relief images, *J. Opt. Soc. Amer.* **58**, 533–539 (April 1968).

11. T. M. Holladay and J. D. Gallatin, Phase control by polarization in coherent spatial filtering, *ibid.* **56**, 869–872 (July 1966).

12. B. R. Brown and A. W. Lohmann, Complex spatial filtering with binary masks, *Appl. Opt.* **5**, 967–969 (June 1966).

13. A. W. Lohmann and D. P. Paris, Computer generated spatial filters for coherent optical data processing, *ibid.* **7**, 651–655 (April 1968).

14. A. Vander Lugt, Signal detection by complex spatial filtering, *IEEE Trans. Information Theory* **IT-10**, 139–145 (April 1964).

15. D. Gabor, Character recognition by holography, *Nature* **208**, 422 (October 30, 1965); see also the note of the same title by B. M. Watrasiewicz, *ibid.* **216**, 302–304 (October 21, 1967).

16. A. Kozma and D. L. Kelly, Spatial filtering for detection of signals submerged in noise, *Appl. Opt.* **4**, 387–392 (April 1965).

17. A. Vander Lugt, F. B. Rotz, and A. Klooster, Jr., Character-reading by optical spatial filtering, OEOIP, pp. 125–141.

18. C. S. Weaver and J. W. Goodman, A technique for optically convolving two functions, *Appl. Opt.* **5**, 1248–1249 (July 1966).

19. W. T. Cathey, Jr., Spatial phase modulation of wavefronts in spatial filtering and holography, *J. Opt. Soc. Amer.* **56**, 1167–1171. (September 1966).

20. A. Vander Lugt, Practical considerations for the use of spatial carrier-frequency filters, *Appl. Opt.* **5**, 1760–1765 (November 1966).

21. A. Vander Lugt and R. H. Mitchel, Technique for measuring modulation transfer functions of recording media, *J. Opt. Soc. Amer.* 57, 372-379 (March 1967).

22. A. Vander Lugt, The effects of small displacements of spatial filters, *Appl. Opt.* **6**, 1221–1225 (July 1967).

23. D. J. Raso, Simplified method to make hologram filters for target recognition, *J. Opt. Soc. Amer.* **58**, 432–433 (March 1968).

24. A. W. Lohmann, Matched filtering with self-luminous objects, *Appl. Opt.* **7**, 561–563 (March 1968).

25. R. A. Binns, A. Dickinson, and B. M. Watrasiewicz, Methods of increasing discrimination in optical filtering, *ibid.* **7**, 1047–1051 (June 1968).

26. A. Dickinson and B. M. Watrasiewicz, Optical filtering applied to postal code reading, CPR, pp. 207–219.

27. R. P. Chambers and J. S. Courtney-Pratt, Bibliography on holograms, Part 1, *J. Soc. Motion Picture Television Engrs.* **75**, 373–435 (April 1966); Part 2, *ibid.* **75**, 759–809 (August 1966).

28. G. W. Stroke, "An Introduction to Coherent Optics and Holography." Academic Press, New York, 1966.

29. J. B. DeVelis and G. O. Reynolds, "Theory and Applications of Holography." Addison-Wesley, Reading, Massachusetts, 1967.

30. J. W. Goodman, "Introduction to Fourier Optics," McGraw-Hill, New York, 1968.

CHAPTER 6

Position-Invariant Operations on Pictures: 3, Applications

6.1. Matched Filtering ("Template Matching")

It is often necessary to determine how well two pictures "match" one another, or to find a part of one picture that matches another picture. These problems arise most commonly in the area of pictorial pattern recognition, particularly when the "patterns" are highly standardized (e.g., printed characters or images of specific objects). Similar problems also arise in map-matching navigation (e.g., star pattern recognition [1]), where it is necessary to find a region on an observed image that matches a reference "map"; and in automatic stereogrammetry, where the two images of the same point on a stereopair of pictures must be identified in order to measure the parallax at that point (see [2] for a brief historical review of work in this area).

One can also consider the converse problem of detecting differences between two pictures, e.g., of the same scene taken at two different times. Even if the two pictures are in perfect registration, this problem of "change detection" can still be nontrivial if one wants to detect *significant* changes, as opposed to changes due to noise, differences in exposure, shadows, etc. For some interesting methods of detecting the existence of a difference between two pictures, see [3, 4].

There are many possible ways of measuring the difference between two functions. For example, one can simply compute their average (absolute or squared) difference, i.e., $\iint |f - g|$ or $\iint (f - g)^2$, divided by the area over which the integration is performed. A more commonly used method is based on the following theorem, which is known as the Schwarz inequality:

THEOREM. For any two integrable, real-valued, nonnegative functions f, g, not identically zero, we have

$$\int fg \le (\int f^2 \int g^2)^{1/2}$$

over any domain of integration (for which the integrals are all defined), with equality holding if and only if $g = cf$ for some constant c.

PROOF. The inequality is equivalent to $(\int fg)^2 \le \int f^2 \int g^2$. Consider the quadratic polynomial $P(z) = (\int f^2)z^2 + 2(\int fg)z + (\int g^2)$. Since $P(z) = \int (fz + g)^2$, we have $P(z) \ge 0$ for all z, and in fact $P(z_0) = 0$ if and only if $fz_0 + g = 0$ identically in the arguments of f and g. If there exists such a z_0, we have $g = -z_0 f$, a constant times f, and then $(\int fg)^2 = z_0^2 \int f^2 = \int f^2 \int g^2$. If not, $P(z)$ has no real roots, which means that its discriminant $(\int fg)^2 - \int f^2 \int g^2$ is strictly negative. ∎

(a)

Figure 6.1. Normalized cross correlations. (a) Binary-valued digital picture (255 by 255 elements) showing "A," "E," "I," and "O."

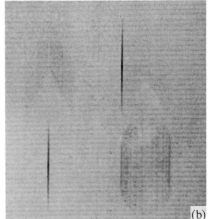

(b)

(b) Cross correlation of the "I" (in a 51-by-51-element window) with Figure 6.1(a).

COROLLARY 1. $\int fg/(\int f^2 \int g^2)^{1/2} \le 1$, and $= 1$ if and only if $g = cf$.

COROLLARY 2

$$\int_{-\infty}^{\infty} \int_{-\infty}^{\infty} f(u, v)g(u + x, v + y) \, du \, dv \Big/ \left(\int_{-\infty}^{\infty} \int_{-\infty}^{\infty} f^2 \int_{-\infty}^{\infty} \int_{-\infty}^{\infty} g^2 \right)^{1/2} \le 1$$

and $= 1$ if and only if $g = cT_{x,y}(f)$. In words: The *normalized cross correlation* of two picture functions f and g can take on the value 1 only for displacements at which g exactly matches f (up to a multiplicative constant).

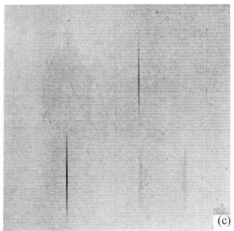

(c)

Figure 6.1. (c) Figure 6.1(b) with each quadrant appropriately normalized.

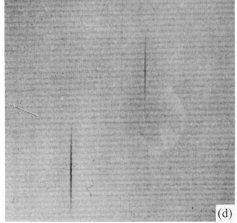

(d)

(d) Nonlinear rescaling (by pointwise squaring) of Figure 6.1(c).

Thus, cross correlating f and g provides a simple method of determining whether they are identical except for translation and multiplication by a constant. This method can be very useful in such pattern recognition tasks as the identification of stylized, noise-free characters of standard size and orientation (but not standardized in position), where only one character is examined at a time (so that a picture contains only a single character); here, one can simply cross correlate the given character with a "template" of each character. The cross correlations of an " I " with an "A," an " E," an " I," and an " O " are shown in Figure 6.1. [The value obtained at a point of perfect match by this method is often not much greater than the values at other points; but the difference can be enhanced by nonlinear scaling, as shown in Figure 6.1(d). In practice nonlinear photographic recording can be used for this purpose.]

If f and g are digital picture functions, we can simply replace the integrals in all of the foregoing by sums. In fact we can state the following discrete analog of the Schwarz inequality: For any two sets of nonnegative real numbers $x_1, \ldots, x_m$ and $y_1, \ldots, y_m$, where neither all the x's are zero nor all the y's zero, we have

$$\sum_{k=1}^{m} x_k y_k \leq \left(\sum_{k=1}^{m} x_k^2 \sum_{k=1}^{m} y_k^2 \right)^{1/2}$$

with equality holding if and only if $y_k = cx_k$ for every k, where c is a constant. To apply this to n-by-n digital pictures, we can simply let $m = n^2$ and let the x's and y's be the gray levels of the picture elements.

EXERCISE 1. Compute the autocorrelation of each of the following binary-valued digital pictures and the cross correlation of each pair of them:

```
000   000   010   010   101   111
010   111   010   111   010   111
000   000   010   010   101   111
```

★ EXERCISE 2. Let (a_{ij}) be an m-by-m "random" binary-valued digital picture in which the probability is p that each a_{ij} is 1, and the a_{ij}'s are independent. (a) What is the expected number of 1's in (a_{ij})? That is, if we generate many such random pictures, what will be the average number 1's in them? (b) If (b_{ij}) is another such picture (but defined using probability q instead of p), what is the expected number of (i, j)'s for which both a_{ij} and b_{ij} are 1? (c) Apply (a) and (b) to compute the expected value of $\sum\sum a_{ij} b_{ij} / (\sum\sum a_{ij}^2 \sum\sum b_{ij}^2)^{1/2}$. (d) If (c_{ij}) is an n-by-n picture defined in the same way as (b_{ij}), with $n > m$, what is the expected value of the (digital) normalized cross correlation of (a_{ij}) and (c_{ij}) for displacements such that (a_{ij}) remains "inside" (c_{ij})? What is the expected number of displacements for which this cross correlation is at least k (where $0 < k \le 1$)?

A more general problem is that of finding the pattern f in the picture g, in the sense that we want $g = cT_{x,y}(f)$ over a certain region, say a region S outside which $f = 0$. If we take S as the region of integration in Corollary 2, the numerator is still $f \otimes g$, and the $\iint f^2$ in the denominator is still the same constant, but the $\iint g^2$ is no longer a constant; instead, it is the integral $\iint g^2(u + x, v + y) \, du \, dv$ for (u, v) in S. Note, however, that this last integral can be regarded as the cross correlation of the characteristic function of S (i.e., the function that is 1 inside S and 0 outside S) with g^2. Thus, "finding f in g" can be accomplished by computing the quotient of two cross correlations. Figure 6.2 illustrates this for the pattern "I."

EXERCISE 3. Carry out this computation, letting f be each of the patterns in Exercise 1 (with S a 3-by-3 square), and g a 15-by-15 digital picture containing all of these patterns. What happens if we use a different S, e.g., a rectangle 3 elements wide by 1 high? (Try this, in particular, for the first three patterns.)

> One usually wants the match between f and g to be "sharp," i.e., one wants the displacements at which f matches g to yield sharp peaks in the normalized cross correlation. This will generally be the case if the pattern f is a line drawing, since f will then match very poorly with itself even if slightly displaced, but it will not be the case if f is a "solid" figure. (On measures of "match goodness," see [5].) The existence of such a peak can be detected, without having to scan the correlogram point by point, by imaging the correlogram on a nonlinear photosensor that responds more strongly when the light falling on it is unevenly distributed [6].

Still more generally, suppose that g contains a "noisy" version of the pattern f, call it $f + h$ (so that the noise is "additive"), and that we want to find this pattern in g by cross correlating a template f_1 with g. If the noise h

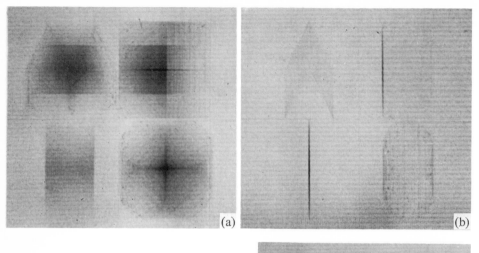

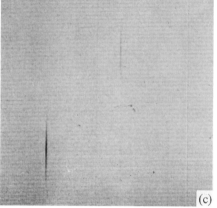

Figure 6..?. Matched filtering by division of correlograms. (a) Cross correlation of a 51-by-51-element window with Figure 6.1(a). (b) Result of dividing Figure 6.1(b) pointwise by the square root of Figure 6.2(a). (c) Nonlinear rescaling (by pointwise squaring) of Figure 6.2(b).

is "independent" of f, in particular if $\iint f_1 h = \iint f_1 \iint h$ for any relative displacement of f_1 and h, it is easy to show that the best f_1 to use for this purpose is f itself. In fact by virtue of our assumption that h and f_1 are independent, $f_1 \otimes h = \iint f_1 \iint h$ is a constant (for all templates f_1 having a given "total transmittance" $\iint f_1$). Hence, $f_1 \otimes (f + h) = f_1 \otimes f + f_1 \otimes h$ is greatest when $f_1 \otimes f$ is greatest, i.e., when $f_1 = f$ (up to translation and a multiplicative constant). Thus, the best template (of a given total transmittance) to use for detecting f, even when it is degraded by additive noise, is still a copy of f itself, i.e., a *matched filter*.

The following alternative treatment of the matched filter problem applies to the case of digital picture functions and normally distributed additive noise. In this case, if the noise-free pattern is (a_{ij}), the probability that (c_{ij}) will be observed is of the form

$$\prod_{i,j=1}^{n} e^{-k(c_{ij}-a_{ij})^2}$$

and if the noise-free pattern is (b_{ij}), the probability can be expressed similarly, with b's replacing a's. To determine which of (a_{ij}) and (b_{ij}) is the more likely, we must thus determine which of these products is greater, which is equivalent (taking logarithms and ignoring constants) to determine whether $\sum_{i,j=1}^{n}[(c_{ij}-b_{ij})^2-(c_{ij}-a_{ij})^2]$ is greater or less than zero. But this sum is just

$$\sum_{i,j=1}^{n}[2c_{ij}(a_{ij}-b_{ij})+b_{ij}^2-a_{ij}^2]$$

Thus if $\sum a_{ij}^2 = \sum b_{ij}^2$, which is analogous to the patterns having the same total transmittance, we need only test which of $\sum c_{ij}a_{ij}$ and $\sum c_{ij}b_{ij}$ is greater; in other words, we should use (a_{ij}) and (b_{ij}) themselves as filters ([7]; compare [8–10]).

If the pictures and patterns under consideration are binary-valued, i.e., they can assume only the values 1 and 0 (transparent and opaque, or white and black), as is approximately the case in many character recognition tasks, one need not use the normalized cross correlation of Corollary 2, which requires division of correlograms. Instead, one can detect a match by cross correlating both a "positive" and a "negative" of the picture and the template and adding, which is much easier to do (e.g., optically) than dividing. Specifically, suppose that the template f has area A, and let its total transmittance ($\iint f$, which is equal in this binary case to the area over which $f = 1$) be T, so that $T \leq A$. If f is cross correlated with the binary picture g, the correlogram $f \otimes g$ can have value T only at displacements for which $g = 1$ at all points where $f = 1$; however, even for such displacements, we can have $g = 1$ at points where $f = 0$. On the other hand, suppose that we cross correlate the negatives f' and g' obtained by interchanging 1's and 0's in f and g, respectively. The total transmittance of the negative template f' is now $A - T$, and

$f' \otimes g'$ can have this value only at displacements for which $g' = 1$ at all points where $f' = 1$; or, equivalently, at displacements for which $g = 0$ at all points where $f = 0$. Thus, for a displacement at which $f \otimes g + f' \otimes g' = T + (A - T) = A$, we must have an exact match of f with g.

Alternatively, one can use $f' \otimes g$, for the second correlogram. This is zero only at displacements for which $g = 0$ at all points where $f' = 1$, i.e., where $f = 0$. Thus, for a displacement at which $f \otimes g - f' \otimes g = T$, we must have an exact match. (This difference can be computed optically, and if desired, the positive and negative templates can be combined into a single template, using the methods described in Section 5.3.) Even more simply, note that

$$f \otimes g - f' \otimes g = 2f \otimes g - (f \otimes g + f' \otimes g) = 2f \otimes g - (f + f') \otimes g,$$

where the second term in the right member is just the cross correlation of a completely transparent template with the picture [11]. This is illustrated, for the pattern "I," in Figure 6.3.

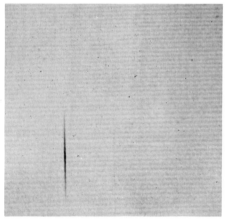

Figure 6.3. Matched filtering of binary-valued patterns by subtraction of correlograms: Pointwise difference of Figures 6.1(b) and 6.2(a), with negative values regarded as zero.

Another way of testing for a match between a binary-valued *digital* picture and a template is to multiply the picture pointwise by shifted copies of itself and its "negative." In fact let the template have the value 1 at $(x_{i_1 j_1}, y_{i_1 j_1}), \ldots, (x_{i_h j_h}, y_{i_h j_h})$, and 0 at $(u_{i_1 j_1}, v_{i_1 j_1}), \ldots, (u_{i_k j_k}, v_{i_k j_k})$; then g matches the template at the displacement (x, y) if and only if $\prod_{\alpha=1}^{h} g(x - x_{i_\alpha j_\alpha}, y - y_{i_\alpha j_\alpha}) \prod_{\beta=1}^{k} (1 - g(x - u_{i_\beta j_\beta}, y - v_{i_\beta j_\beta})) = 1$.

REFERENCES

1. H. W. Sowers, Star pattern recognition—a survey of the literature, AD 421473 (October 1963).
2. C. L. Hobrough, Automation in photogrammetric instruments, *Photogrammetric Engrg*. **31**, 595–603 (July 1965).
3. W. T. Cathey, Jr. and J. G. Doidge, Image comparison by interference, *J. Opt. Soc. Amer*. **56**, 1139–1140 (August 1966).
4. J. E. Rau, Detection of differences in real distributions, *ibid*. **56**, 1490–1494 (November 1966).
5. N. D. Diamantides, Correlation measure of contrast for map matching, *ibid*. **58**, 996–998 (July 1968).
6. J. C. Bliss and H. D. Crane, Relative motion and nonlinear photocells in optical image processing, OEOIP, pp. 615–637.
7. J. L. Harris, Resolving power and decision theory, *J. Opt. Soc. Amer*. **54**, 606–611 (May 1964).
8. C. K. Chow, An optimum character recognition system using decision function, *IRE Trans. Electronic Computers* **EC-6**, 247–254 (December 1957).
9. W. D. Montgomery and P. W. Broome, Spatial filtering, *J. Opt. Soc. Amer*. **52**, 1259–1275 (November 1962).
10. E. A. Trabka and P. G. Roetling, Shape detection using incoherent illumination, *ibid*. **57**, 108–110 (January 1967).
11. J. A. Fitzmaurice, Reading Russian scientific literature, OCR, pp. 61–72.

6.2. Spatial Frequency Filtering and Image Restoration

As indicated in Chapters 4 and 5, another way to convolve a template with a picture is to multiply their Fourier transforms and take the inverse Fourier transform of the product. When we use this approach, we are carrying out the template-matching operation in the "spatial frequency domain" rather than in the "space domain"; i.e., we are performing multiplication and integration operations on the Fourier transform rather than on the original picture. (For references on matched filtering in the spatial frequency domain, see Section 5.4; for an example, see Figure 6.4.)

One of the chief advantages of working in the spatial frequency domain is that a variety of useful picture processing operations can be performed using very simple templates (a more usual term in this context is "filters"). For example (see Figure 6.5), introducing an opaque disk (in optical terms, a "stop") centered on the optical axis has the effect of suppressing low spatial frequencies while "passing" high ones; typically, this will "wash out"

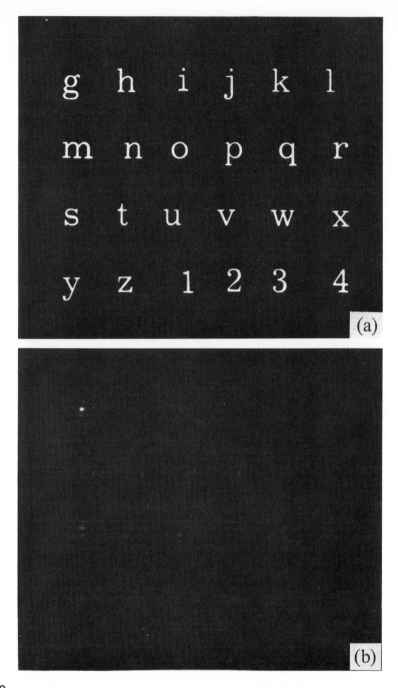

smooth regions on the picture, while preserving sharp edges and fine detail. Conversely, using an annulus as a stop will suppress high frequencies while passing low ones; this will blur the picture. A sector-shaped stop will tend to blur edges that are perpendicular to the direction of the sector. (References on these techniques will be given in Sections 6.4 and 6.5. On the advantages of performing spatial frequency filtering using the logarithm of the picture rather than the picture itself, see [1]). Equivalent operations can, of course, be performed by convolving the original picture with appropriate templates (namely, the inverse Fourier transforms of the stops). A "stop" (or more generally, a filter) that is real and symmetrical about the origin (as is, e.g., a disk, an annulus, or a symmetrical pair of sectors) has an inverse Fourier transform that is also real, so that convolution (equivalent here to cross correlation, since the transform is symmetrical) of the picture with the transform can be done optically using the methods described in Section 5.3.

An important application of spatial frequency filtering is to the problem of "image restoration." Suppose that a picture has been obtained through some imaging or transmission process that has degraded it. If the degradation can be mathematically inverted, it is, in principle, possible to undo it and "restore" the picture to its original condition. In particular, suppose that the degradation is a position-invariant linear operation, say that of convolving some g with the original picture f, so that the degraded picture is $f * g$. Then, if we take the Fourier transform of $f * g$, we obtain FG, the product of the Fourier transforms of f and g; and if we now simply divide by G and take the inverse Fourier transform, we have restored the original f.

We can obtain G, at least approximately, by allowing the degradation to operate on a one-point picture and taking the Fourier transform of the result. In practice the degradation is rarely a position-invariant linear operation; we can think of it as also involving noise, and the restoration process is usually highly sensitive to this noise.

Figure 6.4. Optical matched filtering in the spatial frequency domain. (a) Array of alphanumerics. (b) Inverse Fourier transform of the product of the Fourier transforms of the array and the letter "g."

Reprinted from A. Vander Lugt, Signal detection by complex spatial filtering, *IEEE Trans. Information Theory* **IT-10**, 145 (April 1964).

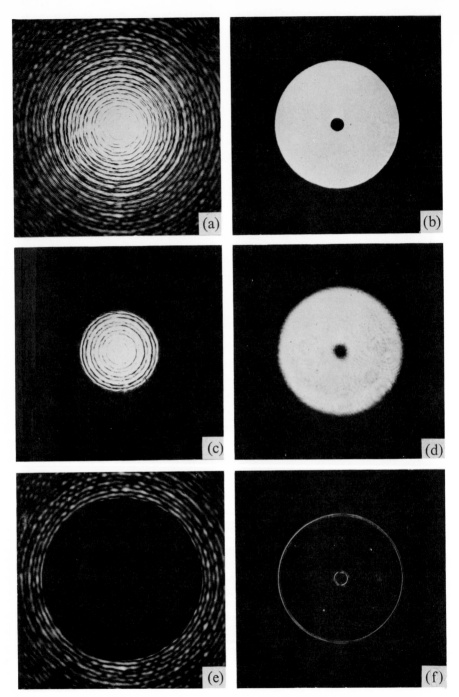

82

Nevertheless, useful results can often be obtained by dividing by G in those spatial-frequency ranges where the signal-to-noise ratio is high. For an example of a restoration obtained in this way, see Figure 6.6.

For a good introduction to these concepts, see [2]; for other and related references, see [3–10].

EXERCISE. Under what circumstances can a linear digital local operation defined by matrix multiplication (Section 4.2, Exercise 3) be inverted?

REFERENCES

1. A. V. Oppenheim, R. W. Schafer, and T. G. Stockham, Jr., Nonlinear filtering of multiplied and convolved signals, *Proc. IEEE* **56**, 1264–1291 (August 1968).
2. J. L. Harris, Image evaluation and restoration, *J. Opt. Soc. Amer.* **56**, 569–574 (May 1966).
3. J. Tsujiuchi, Correction of optical images by compensation of aberrations and by spatial frequency filtering, "Progress in Optics" (E. Wolf, ed.), Vol. 2, pp. 131–180. Wiley, New York, 1963.
4. J. L. Harris, Diffraction and resolving power, *J. Opt. Soc. Amer.* **54**, 931–936 (July 1964).
5. B. L. McGlamery, Restoration of turbulence-degraded images, *ibid.* **57**, 293–297 (March 1967).
6. C. W. Helstrom, Image restoration by the method of least squares, *ibid.* **57**, 297–303 (March 1967).
7. A. W. Lohmann, D. P. Paris, and H. W. Werlich, A computer generated spatial filter, applied to code translation, *Appl. Opt.* **6**, 1139–1140 (June 1967).
8. D. Slepian, Linear least-squares filtering of distorted images, *J. Opt. Soc. Amer.* **57**, 918–922 (July 1967); see also D. Slepian, Restoration of photographs blurred by image motion, *Bell System Tech. J.* **46**, 2353–2362 (December 1967).

Figure 6.5. High-pass and low-pass optical spatial frequency filtering (the original object is a 3 mm-diameter hole with an 0.3 mm stop at its center). (a) Power spectrum of object recorded in Fourier transform plane. (b) Inverse Fourier transform of Fourier transform of object (no filtering). (c) Power spectrum with low-pass filter superimposed. (d) Result of low-pass filtering. (e) Power spectrum with high-pass filter superimposed. (f) Result of high-pass filtering.

9. C. K. Rushforth and R. W. Harris, Restoration, resolution, and noise, *ibid.* **58**, 539–545 (April 1968).
10. B. R. Frieden, Optimum, nonlinear processing of noisy images, *ibid.* **58**, 1272–1275 (September 1968).

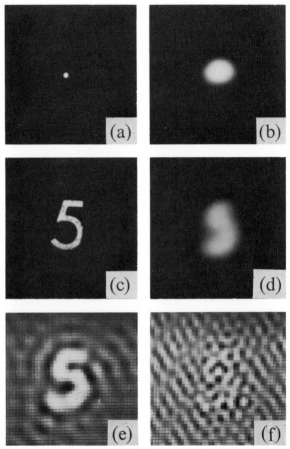

Figure 6.6. Image restoration. (a) "One-point" picture without degradation. (b) "One-point" picture with degradation. (c) "5," undegraded. (d) "5," degraded. (e) "5," restored (the division was done only for spatial frequencies below 2 cycles/mm). (f) Result of doing the division for spatial frequencies up to 3 cycles/mm.

Reprinted from B. L. McGlamery, Restoration of turbulence-degraded images, *J. Opt. Soc. Amer.* **57**, 295 (March 1967).

6.3. Measurement of Image Quality

Whenever a picture is converted from one form to another, e.g., photographically copied, optically imaged, scanned, or displayed, one can ask how faithfully the information contained in the input picture is preserved in the output picture. On a subjective level, one can also ask about the "quality" of the output as a representation of the original.

The spread and transfer functions defined in Section 4.4 provide detailed information about the "blurredness" of an output picture relative to the input picture. For many purposes, however, one wants measures of blurredness that are single numbers rather than functions. Two quantities commonly used for this purpose are *resolution* and *acutance*. The first of these relates to the distinguishability of close objects, while the second is concerned with the sharpness of edges. (These quantities are not necessarily interdependent; to see this, let ϕ_1 and ϕ_2 be operations having point spread functions that are, respectively, "top-hatlike" and "conelike." Evidently, close objects will be harder to resolve in a ϕ_1 image, but edges in it will be sharper than in a ϕ_2 image.)

Specific measures of resolution can be defined by specifying the objects to be "resolved" (i.e., seen as distinct) as well as the contrast that must exist between the objects and the spaces between them before they can be regarded as resolved. The most commonly used objects for this purpose are the familiar bar chart (closely spaced sets of parallel rectangles) and the Landolt "C" (an annulus with a narrow cut in it).

Acutance is usually measured by the average of the squared "steepness" (i.e., the rate of change of the gray level) across an edge, divided by the total contrast across the edge. This measure can be expressed in the form

$$\int_a^b (df/dx)^2/[|f(b) - f(a)|]$$

where a and b are points that lie close to and on opposite sides of the edge. Experiments have shown that this measure correlates well with the subjective sensation of edge "sharpness." (For historical reviews of these concepts, see [1, 2]; compare [3].)

EXERCISE 1. Let the picture function f be blurred by averaging its gray level over a circular neighborhood of radius r at each point. If f contains a sharp edge, e.g., $f = 1$ for $x \leq 0$ and $f = 0$ for $x > 0$, what is the acutance of this edge in the blurred picture? If f contains a pair of parallel strips, e.g., $f = 1$ for $0 \leq x \leq 1$ and $2 \leq x \leq 3$ and $f = 0$ elsewhere, what are the maximum and the minimum gray levels in the blurred picture in the region $0 \leq x \leq 3$?

Picture conversion processes are subject to many different types of noise. Unfortunately, little work has been done on the development of mathematical models for pictorial (i.e., two-dimensional) noise. Some types of noise can be regarded, at least approximately, as additive, but other types (such as "grain noise," discussed below) cannot. (On the general subject of random geometrical processes, see M. G. Kendall and P. A. P. Moran, "Geometrical Probability." Hafner, New York, 1963.)

An important special type of pictorial noise, which has been extensively studied, is photographic *granularity*. Conventional photographic media can be regarded as consisting of randomly scattered clumps of "grains"; the gray level of a region on a photograph is determined by the number of developed grains per unit area over the region. The reason that a photograph f appears to contain gray levels, rather than appearing binary-valued, is that one can never measure (or see) f "at a point"; rather, one can only measure $\iint f$ over some region ("aperture") of finite size. A photograph of an object that has a constant gray level will appear to have a fluctuating gray level because of the presence of the grains. Granularity is a property related to the magnitude and spatial extent of these fluctuations. The following are some specific measures of granularity [4–10]:

1. *RMS granularity and Selwyn granularity.* A simple measure of granularity is the standard deviation of the gray level: $\sigma_f = [\iint (\bar{f} - f)^2]^{1/2}$, where $\bar{f} = \iint f$ is the average gray level. This of course depends on the size A of the aperture over which f is measured; in fact it can be shown that σ_f is approximately proportional to $1/\sqrt{A}$. Thus, the quantity $\sigma_f \sqrt{A}$ is approximately constant; it is called Selwyn granularity.

2. *Syzygetic density difference.* Another proposed measure of granularity is the syzygetic density difference, defined as $\Delta f / \Delta x$, where Δx is the distance on the photograph that corresponds to the distance between two adjacent cones in the fovea of the eye.

3. *Autocorrelation.* Since granularity depends on the sizes of clumps of grains, it can be studied by examining the autocorrelation of f. By Schwarz' inequality (Section 6.1), this takes on its maximum value $\iint f^2$ at zero displacement; and if there were no granularity, it would always have this value

for a constant picture. The rapidity with which its value drops under a small displacement is a measure of the coarseness of the grain clumps.

4. *Power spectrum.* Alternatively, granularity can be studied by examining the spatial frequencies that are present in a constant picture. This approach is closely related to that using the autocorrelation, since (Section 4.3) the power spectrum is its Fourier transform.

★EXERCISE 2. For the binary-valued random digital picture defined in Exercise 2, Section 6.1, compute (a) the rms granularity as a function of p and the number of elements in the aperture (assuming that the aperture is entirely inside the picture), (b) the Selwyn granularity, and (c) the expected value of the autocorrelation for a nonzero displacement (ignoring the fact that the picture will only partly overlap itself when shifted).

Various unified measures of picture quality, which reflect both blurredness and noisiness, have been proposed. In particular it has been suggested that information capacity can be regarded as a measure of quality ([11]; see also [1], Section 2.1). It should be pointed out, however, that a blurred picture that can be "restored" (Section 6.2) contains as much information as the original picture, but is certainly not of equal quality in any ordinary sense of the term.

REFERENCES

1. F. H. Perrin, Methods of appraising photographic systems, *J. Soc. Motion Picture Television Engrs.* **69**, 151–156 (March 1960); *ibid.* **69**, 239–249 (April 1960).
2. G. C. Brock, Reflections on thirty years of image evaluation, *Phot. Sci. Engrg.* **11**, 356–362 (September-October 1967).
3. P. G. Roetling, E. A. Trabka, and R. E. Kinzly, Theoretical prediction of image quality, *J. Opt. Soc. Amer.* **58**, 342–346 (March 1968).
4. P. Fellgett, Concerning photographic grain, signal-to-noise ratio, and information, *ibid.* **43**, 271–282 (April 1953).
5. R. C. Jones, New method of describing and measuring the granularity of photographic materials, *ibid.* **45**, 799–808 (October 1955).
6. H. J. Zweig, Autocorrelation and granularity, *ibid.* **46**, 802–820 (October 1956); *ibid.* **49**, 238–244 (March 1959).
7. A. Marriage and E. Pitts, Relation between granularity and autocorrelation, *ibid.* **46**, 1019–1027 (December 1956); *ibid.* **47**, 321–326 (April 1957).

8. E. L. O'Neill, Graininess and entropy, *ibid.* **48**, 945–947 (December 1958).
9. G. A. Fry, Coarseness of photographic grain, *ibid.* **53**, 361–367 (March 1963).
10. K. V. Vendrovskii, M. A. Aingorn, and I. G. Minkevich, The graininess of photographic images, *Usp. Nauchn. Fotogr.* **11**, 171–221 (1966).
11. R. Shaw, The application of Fourier techniques and information theory to the assessment of photographic image quality, *Phot. Sci. Engrg.* **6**, 281–286 (September-October 1962).
12. K. V. Chibisov, *et al.*, eds. "Quality of the Photographic Image" (Advances in Scientific Photography, Vol. X). "SCIENCE," Moscow-Leningrad, 1964; available in translation as AD 460800.

6.4. Image Enhancement: "Smoothing"

In this section we consider position-invariant operations (not necessarily linear) that can be used to "smooth" a picture in order to suppress noise that may be present in it.

a. *Averaging over a Neighborhood*

One can smooth a picture by simply replacing its value at each point by the average of the values over a neighborhood of the point. Assuming that the same neighborhood is used at each point, this is evidently a position-invariant (indeed, a local) operation; in fact it is just the convolution of the picture with a function that has the value $1/A$ inside the neighborhood and 0 outside, where A is the area of the neighborhood. (Averaging operations can be performed optically in very simple ways, e.g., by imaging the picture slightly out of focus, or copying it slightly out of contact. In the former case, to ensure that position invariance holds, at least approximately, the picture must not extend too far from the optical axis.) For examples of the results of averaging a picture using various neighborhood sizes, see Figure 6.7. More generally, one can take a weighted average, e.g., an average in which the points of the neighborhood have weights that decrease as their distances from the center increase.

It may sometimes be advantageous [1] to use a neighborhood whose size varies from point to point. For example, one can smooth a binary-valued picture containing only a scattering of 1's by finding, at each point, the smallest (say) circular neighborhood that contains a prespecified number of 1's and giving that point in the output picture a gray level inversely proportional to the area of that neighborhood. Note that this operation is no longer linear.

Figure 6.7. Smoothing by averaging over a neighborhood. In the
original binary-valued picture (a), the probabilities of black
elements in the four quadrants are 0.1, 0.2, 0.4, and 0.8,
respectively. Each smoothed version is obtained by averaging over
a square neighborhood oriented at 45° and of radius 1, 2, 4, 8, and
16 in parts (b–f), respectively.

To smooth a picture without blurring it, one can use other nonlinear operations that involve averaging. The simplest class of such operations combines averaging with thresholding. For example, one can clean up "pepper and salt" noise (isolated dark points in light regions and vice versa) by making a point "whiter" if the average gray level in some neighborhood of it exceeds its gray level by more than some threshold; the procedure is similar for making a point blacker [2]. This method is illustrated in Figure 6.8.

Figure 6.8.

A nonlinear smoothing method applied to the cloud-cover picture of Figure 3.1(a). Let the neighbors of the element E be denoted by

$$A \quad B \quad C$$
$$D \quad E \quad F$$
$$G \quad H \quad I$$

If $|E - (A + B + C + D + F + G + H + I)/8|$ (see Figure 6.11) is higher than $\frac{1}{4}$ of the maximum possible value, replace E by $(A + B + C + D + F + G + H + I)/8$; otherwise, leave E unchanged. Note that this process does not blur the picture, but tends to smooth out, e.g., the white spots and streaks near the upper fiducial marks.

90

Another approach [3] is to average the picture isotropically at points where "edges" are not present, but to average it only in the direction along the edge where an edge is present (on edge detection criteria, see the next section).

★ EXERCISE 1. If the random picture defined in Exercise 2, Section 6.1 is smoothed by changing an element from 0 to 1 if more than m of its eight neighbors are 1's, and vice versa, how many elements will change? How will the rms granularity of the picture be affected? (Ignore effects at the border of the picture.)

★ EXERCISE 2. If the same random picture is smoothed using the variable-neighborhood scheme described earlier, where the neighborhood is chosen just large enough to contain k 1's and border effects are ignored, what is the rms granularity of the result as a function of p and k?

b. *Averaging of Multiple Copies*

By averaging together a set of independent copies of a noisy picture, one can "attenuate" the noise without attenuating the picture itself ([4]; see also [5, 6]). In principle the averaging can be done by optical superposition, but since this requires perfect registration, it is practical only if n is small. For an example of the effect of superposition, see Figure 6.9.

> To understand the principle underlying the superposition method, suppose that the picture f has been degraded by additive noise whose value is normally distributed with mean 0 and variance σ^2. (The distribution can, of course, only be approximately normal, since there are no negative gray levels.) The value of the noisy picture at any given point (x, y) will thus be normally distributed with mean $f(x, y)$ and variance σ^2. Suppose that n copies of the picture can be made in such a way that the samples of the noise in the copies are all independent. Then the value of the average of the n copies at (x, y) is normally distributed with mean $f(x, y)$ and variance σ^2/n. (See, e.g., E. Parzen, "Modern Probability Theory and Its Applications," p. 37. Wiley, New York, 1960.)

Similarly, the image of a symmetric object can be enhanced by superposing copies of a single picture that, e.g., have been rotated in such a way as

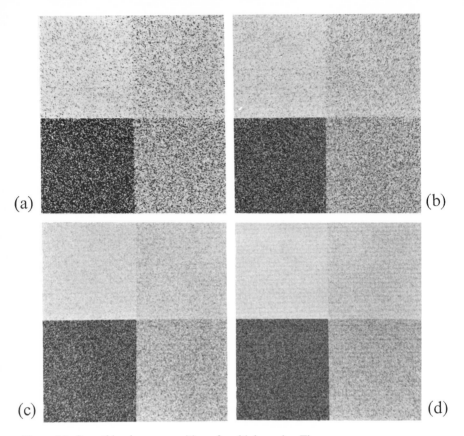

(a)   (b)

(c)   (d)

Figure 6.9. Smoothing by superposition of multiple copies. The numbers of copies in parts (a- d) are 2, 4, 8, and 16, respectively. [The pictures that were superimposed are versions of Figure 6.7(a).]

to take the object into itself [7, 8]. [On *multiplicative* superposition of multiple copies of a picture (or passing light repeatedly through a single copy) as a method of increasing contrast, see [9, 10]; compare [11].]

c. *Bandpass Spatial Frequency Filtering*

As pointed out in Section 6.2, another way to smooth a picture is to suppress the high spatial frequencies from its Fourier transform and take the inverse transform of the result. Such "low-pass" spatial filtering will also blur the picture, and so would usually be undesirable. However, it is sometimes possible to suppress noise from a picture by deleting a selected *band* of spatial frequencies while leaving enough at high frequencies to keep edges unblurred. In particular if a picture contains periodic noise (e.g., a television image can be regarded as a continuous picture on which a grid of parallel lines— namely, the blank lines between the raster lines—has been superimposed), the noise can usually be suppressed by deleting appropriate small regions from the Fourier transform of the noisy picture. Similarly, a halftone can be converted into a continuous picture in this way; and in fact graininess can be effectively smoothed out of a picture (photograph or other quantum-limited image), even though the grains are not regularly spaced, by attenuating the spatial frequency band corresponding to the grain sizes ([12–16]; see also [17]).

d. *Introduction of Noise*

A picture can be blurred by introducing noise into it; this operation can be "statistically position-invariant" in the sense that the frequency distribution of the noise is the same at every point. Two simple examples are:

1. *Additive noise.* The gray level at each point is increased or decreased by an amount selected in accordance with a given frequency distribution (typically, peaked at zero).

2. *Random walk noise* [18]. Each point is interchanged with another point at a distance selected in accordance with a given frequency distribution (typically, peaked at zero) and in a randomly chosen direction.

REFERENCES

1. S. M. Pizer and H. G. Vetter, Perception and processing of medical radioisotope scans, PPR, pp. 147–156.
2. G. P. Dinneen, Programming pattern recognition, *WJCC* pp. 94–100 (March 1955).
3. R. E. Graham, Snow removal—a noise stripping process for picture signals, *IRE Trans. Information Theory* **IT-8**, 129–144 (February 1962).
4. R. Kohler and H. Howell, Photographic image enhancement by superimposition of multiple images, *Phot. Sci. Engrg.* **7**, 241–245 (July-August 1963).
5. R. G. Hart, Electron microscopy of unstained biological material: the polytropic montage, *Science* **159**, 1464–1467 (March 29, 1968).
6. T. J. Janssens, G. C. Kozlowski, and A. J. Luther, Real time digital subtraction and enhancement of video pictures, *J. Soc. Photo-Opt. Instr. Engrs.* **6**, 120–124 (April-May 1968).

7. H. O. Agrawal, J. W. Kent, and D. M. MacKay, Rotation technique in electron microscopy of viruses, *Science* **148**, 638–640 (April 30, 1965).

8. R. S. Norman, Rotation technique in radially symmetric electron micrographs: mathematical analysis, *ibid.* **152**, 1238–1239 (May 27, 1966).

9. M. Clopeau, The printing of underexposed photographs by means of "optical contrasters," *Phot. Sci. Engrg.* **5**, 175–180 (May-June 1961).

10. M. Clopeau and K. Raymond, Optical procedure for intensifiying photographic negatives of low contrast, *Compt. Rend., Ser. B* **263**, 287–290 (July 25, 1966).

11. G. T. Bauer, The use of partially transparent plates to increase the contrast of images, *Appl. Opt.* **5**, 1361–1364 (September 1966).

12. H. Thiry, Some qualitative and quantitative results on spatial filtering of granularity, *ibid.* **3**, 39–43 (January 1964).

13. P. G. Roetling, Effects of signal-dependent granularity, *J. Opt. Soc. Amer.* **55**, 67–71 (January 1965).

14. F. C. Billingsley, Processing Ranger and Mariner photography, *J. Soc. Photo-Opt. Instr. Engrs.* **4**, 147–155 (April-May 1966).

15. R. Nathan, Picture enhancement for the moon, Mars, and man, PPR, pp. 239–266.

16. E. Efron, Image processing by digital systems, *Photogrammetric Engrg.* **34**, 1058–1062 (October 1968).

17. L. G. Callahan and W. M. Brown, One- and two-dimensional processing in line scanning systems, *Appl. Opt.* **2**, 401–407 (April 1963).

18. B. W. White, The computer as a pattern generator for perceptual research, *Behavior. Sci.* **6**, 252–259 (July 1961).

6.5. Image Enhancement: "Sharpening"

Just as one can smooth or blur a picture in a variety of ways, so there are many ways to "sharpen" or "deblur" a picture. For example, this can be done by quantizing the picture ("clipping"), by reproducing it xerographically or on a high-contrast photographic medium, or by high-pass spatial frequency filtering (e.g., [1]). In this section we describe a number of other methods of sharpening pictures.

a. *The Gradient*

Since integration (or averaging) blurs a picture, a natural approach to deblurring is to perform some sort of differentiation operation. If deblurring is required only in some particular direction, one can simply take a directional derivative. For most purposes, however, one wants to deblur in *every* direction; this can be accomplished by taking the derivative in the *gradient* direction, i.e., the direction in which the gray level changes fastest, at each point

[2]. For a well-behaved function, this maximal directional derivative is equal to the square root of the sum of the squares of the derivatives in any pair of orthogonal directions, e.g., $[(\partial f/\partial x)^2 + (\partial f/\partial y)^2]^{1/2}$. For a digital picture, one would approximate the derivatives by differences, e.g., $[(a_{i+1,j} - a_{ij})^2 + (a_{i,j+1} - a_{ij})^2]^{1/2}$. [Similar results are obtained by using a sum of absolute values of differences rather than the square root of the sum of their squares. A more symmetrical scheme would be to use differences of pairs of gray levels on opposite sides of (i,j); see [2] in Section 6.4 and [17] for examples of such schemes.] A typical digital "gradient" is illustrated in Figure 6.10.

★ EXERCISE. (a) Ignoring border effects, what is the expected value of the digital gradient for the random picture? (b) If we juxtapose two such random pictures, generated using probabilities p_1 and p_2, respectively, what is the expected value of the gradient at a point along the edge where the pictures meet? (c) Carry out the analogous computations for the other "difference" operations defined in this section (Laplacian, directional differencing, "statistical" differencing).

> Directional derivatives (of both first and higher orders) can be, at least approximately, obtained optically by convolving the given picture with appropriate templates ([18], Section 5.3; [13], Section 5.4.) There are also simple electronic methods of obtaining approximations to two orthogonal derivatives, or to the gradient derivative, in a single scan of a picture, using an "isotropic scan" [2] that combines two orthogonal scan patterns oriented at $\pm 45°$. Since the gradient at a point is approximately proportional to the difference between the maximum and minimum gray levels on a small circle centered at the point, it can also be computed electronically by performing a "helical" scan of the picture (the spot moves rapidly around a small circle whose center shifts slowly across the picture) and measuring the amplitude modulation of the resulting video signal at the frequency of the circular motion.

b. *The Laplacian*

Another useful combination of derivatives is the *Laplacian* $\partial^2 f/\partial x^2 + \partial^2 f/\partial y^2$ ([2]; compare [3]). For a digital picture an analogous expression is

$$[(a_{ij} - a_{i-1,j}) - (a_{i+1,j} - a_{ij})] + [(a_{ij} - a_{i,j-1}) - (a_{i,j+1} - a_{ij})]$$
$$= 4a_{ij} - (a_{i-1,j} + a_{i+1,j} + a_{i,j-1} + a_{i,j+1})$$

95

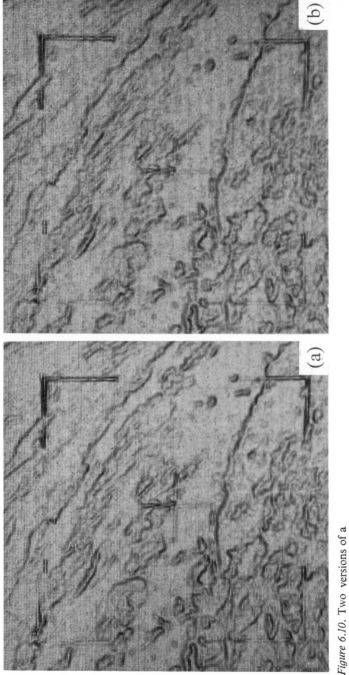

Figure 6.10. Two versions of a
digital gradient applied to the cloud-cover picture of Figure 3.1(a):

(a) $([(A+B+C)-(G+H+I)]^2+[(A+D+G)-(C+F+I)]^2)^{1/2}$
(b) $|(A+B+C)-(G+H+I)|+|(A+D+G)-(C+F+I)|$

(the notation is as in Figure 6.8). Since the gray level in this picture
rarely changes very abruptly, gradients based on differences of *adjacent*
elements would have generally lower values.

Note that this is proportional to the difference between the gray level at the point and the average gray level in an "annulus" centered at the point (compare [12], Section 5.1; see also [4, 5]). We can thus approximate the Laplacian by convolving the picture with a template having a positive peak that is surrounded by a negative annular "valley," with the values chosen so that the integral of the template is zero (i.e., the negative part cancels the positive part). It can be verified that the convolution of such a template with a picture is zero in regions where the picture is constant or linear but not at "edges" across which the second derivative is nonzero. A digital Laplacian is illustrated in Figure 6.11. [Neurons that seem to perform this type of opera-

Figure 6.11.

A digital Laplacian applied to Figure 3.1(a):

$$|E - (A + B + C + D + F + G + H + I)/8|$$

tion on the retinal image have been found in the visual systems of a number of animals. These neurons have "receptor fields" on the retina with "excitatory" centers surrounded by "inhibitory" annuli or vice versa. See [6], which cites numerous references on the visual systems of the cat, crab (*limulus*), frog, pigeon, and rabbit.] Under some circumstances [7], it may be advantageous to perform the Laplacian computation repeatedly.

> Special-purpose devices have been built that simulate visual information processing in the crab, frog, and pigeon. For references, see BPSS; M. B. Herscher and T. P. Kelley, Functional electronic model of the frog retina, *IEEE Trans. Military Electronics* **MIL-7**, 98–103 (April-July 1963); M. P. Beddoes, D. J. Connor, and Z. A. Melzak, Simulation of a visual receptor network, *IEEE Trans. Bio-Medical Engineering* **B-ME-12**, 136–138 (July-October 1965); and H. L. Oestreicher and D. L. Moore, eds., "Cybernetic Problems in Bionics." Gordon and Breach, New York, 1968.

An especially simple method of computing the Laplacian optically is based on the fact that taking the Laplacian of f is approximately equivalent to subtracting from f a blurred copy of itself. This observation is the principle underlying a standard photographic technique known as *unsharp masking*, in which a positive transparency and a blurred negative transparency of the same picture are superimposed, and the light passing through both is recorded. It is even possible to use the same transparency as both the positive and the negative by using a quenchable phosphor screen (see Section 5.3) as shown in Figure 6.12 [8, 9]. Here, if the infrared source were turned off, the phos-

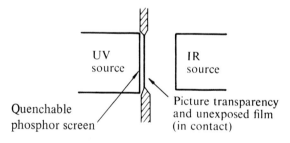

Figure 6.12. One-transparency unsharp masking.

phor would be uniformly bright, and the picture would be exactly copied on the unexposed film, which is in contact with it. However, since the infrared source is on, the infrared light passes through the film without affecting it and dims the phosphor in a pattern that is an out-of-focus copy of the picture (it is out of focus since there is a space between the picture transparency and the phosphor screen). Thus, the phosphor becomes a luminous out-of-focus negative of the picture; consequently, when the light from the phosphor passes through the picture transparency to be recorded on the film, the result is the same as if there were a uniformly bright phosphor and two superimposed transparencies of the picture, one positive and one out-of-focus negative.

Several simple methods of computing an approximate Laplacian by scanning a picture also deserve mention here [10–12]. The basic idea is to simultaneously scan with two scanning spots, one fine and one coarse, and subtract the resulting signals electronically. More simply, one can use a single spot whose focus is modulated at a rate much faster than the scanning motion; if the signal is delayed by half the period of the focus modulation and subtracted from itself, the result is equivalent to subtracting a coarse from a fine spot. Still more simply, one can image the scanning spot on the picture through a nonachromatic lens, so that it is in focus for colors at one end of the spectrum and out of focus for those at the other end. If the color separation method described at the end of Section 5.3 is now used, the two channels "see" fine and coarse spots, respectively. Another approach is to use the optical system shown in Figure 6.13; here, since there is a space between the (fine) flying spot and the transparency f, the photosensor sees a scan of f by an out-of-focus spot. The resulting signal is used to reduce the brightness of the flying spot, so that f is actually illuminated by an out-of-focus negative of itself. Thus, what the lens images on plane P is the superposition of f

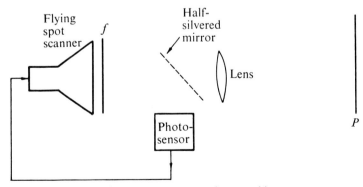

Figure 6.13. Alternative method of one-transparency unsharp masking.

(in focus) and a negative of f (out of focus). (See [13] for a comparison of unsharp masking with other techniques in which the blurred image is produced by lateral shift or by "ring smear" rather than by defocus.)

c. Directional Derivatives and Differences

Edges or lines in a particular direction can be emphasized while all others are attenuated or suppressed, by performing a suitable differentiation or differencing operation in the orthogonal direction. For example, to emphasize edges having slope m, one can convolve the picture with a template that is positive in a strip just on one side of the line $y = mx$ and negative in a strip on the other side; the values are chosen so that they cancel when the template is integrated. (See Figure 6.14 for the results of applying such operations, in the horizontal and vertical directions, to a digital picture.) Similarly, to emphasize lines of slope m, one can use a template having a positive "ridge" centered on the line $y = mx$, with a negative "valley" immediately on each side of the ridge. [Neurons that seem to have "receptor fields" of these types have been found in the visual cortexes of various mammals (for references, see [6]). Note that the summations over strips that are used in these edge and line detectors can be accomplished by shifting (in the direction of $y = mx$) and integrating. This suggests an approach to the detection of straight edges and lines based on self-congruence under shifting; on the possibility that this method is used in the human visual system, see [14, 15].] For some purposes, line-detector "templates" that are multiplicative rather than additive may be preferable [16].

d. Statistical Differencing

Rather than differencing by simply subtracting the (average) gray levels in two neighboring regions (point and annulus, two neighboring strips, etc.), one can compare the *frequency distributions* of the gray levels in the two regions. The following are two examples of this approach:

1. Let $\bar{f}$ be obtained by blurring (i.e., averaging) f over a neighborhood at each point, and let σ be the standard deviation of the gray levels of f over the neighborhood, i.e.,

$$\sigma(x, y) = \left[\iint_{N(x, y)} (f - \bar{f})^2 \right]^{1/2}$$

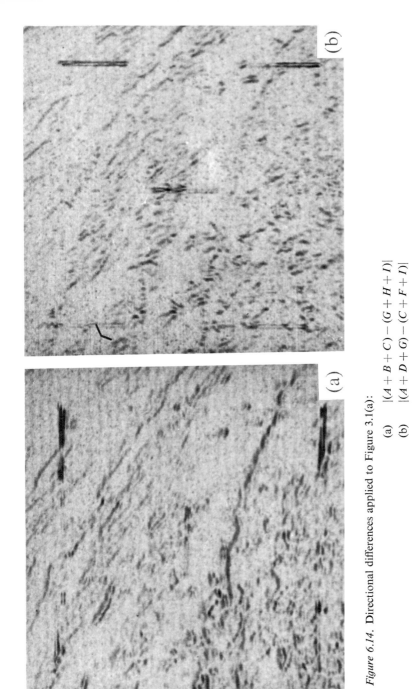

Figure 6.14. Directional differences applied to Figure 3.1(a):

(a) $|(A + B + C) - (G + H + I)|$
(b) $|(A + D + G) - (C + F + I)|$

where N is the neighborhood. Then, rather than working with the Laplacian $f - \bar{f}$, one can work with $(f - \bar{f})/\sigma$; this will be largest at "isolated points" (i.e., points having contrasting neighborhoods over which the gray level is approximately constant), and will not be large if the neighborhood contains many points at each end of the gray scale. For the case in which the neighborhood is a relatively large annulus, see [17, 18]; see also [6], Section 8.4.

2. Let D_1 and D_2 be the frequency distributions of the gray levels in the two regions; one can use $\int |D_1 - D_2|$ to measure the "degree of edge" between the regions [19].

> The following one-dimensional statistical edge-detection criterion applies to the case of a digital picture that is systematically scanned, e.g., in a TV raster. Given the run length and noise statistics for the class of pictures to which the given picture belongs, one can compute the conditional probabilities that two successive elements have the same gray level, given that they belong to the same or different runs. By Bayes' theorem, one can thus compute the conditional probability that two given consecutive elements belong to different runs, i.e., lie on opposite sides of an edge. If this probability exceeds $\frac{1}{2}$, one can assume that an edge has been crossed even though the elements have the same gray level; conversely, if the probability is less than $\frac{1}{2}$, but the elements have different gray levels, one can assume that this difference is due to noise, and can then change the gray levels to eliminate the noise [20].

REFERENCES

1. K. G. Birch, A spatial frequency filter to remove zero frequency, *Optica Acta* **15**, 113–127 (March-April 1967).
2. L. S. G. Kovasznay and H. M. Joseph, Image processing, *Proc. IRE* **43**, 560–570 (May 1955).
3. J. J. Kulikowski, Adaptive visual signal preprocessor with a finite number of states, *IEEE Trans. Systems Science and Cybernetics* **SSC-2**, 96–101 (December 1966).
4. W. K. Taylor, Pattern recognition by means of automatic analogue apparatus, *Proc. IEE* **106B**, 198–209 (March 1959).
5. G. Nagy, Preliminary investigation of techniques for automated reading of unformatted test, *Comm. ACM* **11**, 480–487 (July 1968).

6. F. Ratliff, "Mach Bands: Quantitative Studies on Neural Networks in the Retina." Holden-Day, San Francisco, California, 1965.
7. D. A. Bell, Computer aided design of image processing techniques, CPR, pp. 282–289.
8. A. J. Watson, The Fluoro-Dodge method for contrast control, *Photogrammetric Engrg.* **24**, 638–643 (September 1958).
9. A. B. Clarke, A photographic edge-isolation technique, *ibid.* **28**, 393–399 (July 1962).
10. S. W. Levine and H. Mate, Selected electronic techniques for image enhancement, Paper No. II, "Proceedings, Image Enhancement Seminar," Soc. Phot. Instr. Engrs., Redondo Beach, California, March 1963.
11. D. R. Craig, Disenhancement—a negative approach to a positive problem, Paper No. V, *ibid.*
12. A. J. Hannum, Techniques for electronic image enhancement, Paper No. VII, *ibid.*
13. J. D. Armitage, A. W. Lohmann, and R. B. Herrick, Absolute contrast enhancement, *Appl. Opt.* **4**, 445–451 (April 1965).
14. J. R. Platt, Functional geometry and the determination of patterns in mosaic receptors, "Information Theory in Biology," pp. 371–398. Pergamon Press, New York, 1958.
15. J. R. Platt, How a random array of cells can learn to tell whether a straight line is straight, "Principles of Self-Organization" (H. von Foerster and G. W. Zopf, Jr., eds.), pp. 315–323. Pergamon Press, New York, 1962.
16. J. R. Parks, J. R. Elliott, and G. Cowin, Simulation of an alphanumeric character recognition system for unsegmented low quality print, CPR, pp. 95–105.
17. W. S. Holmes, H. R. Leland, and G. E. Richmond, Design of a photo interpretation automaton, *FJCC* pp. 27–35 (December 1962).
18. W. S. Holmes, Automatic photointerpretation and target location, *Proc. IEEE* **54**, 1679–1686 (December 1966.)
19. J. L. Muerle and D. C. Allen, Experimental evaluation of techniques for automatic segmentation of objects in a complex scene, PPR, pp. 3–13.
20. M. H. Kubba, Automatic picture detail detection in the presence of random noise, *Proc. IEEE* **51**, 1518–1523 (November 1963); see also the comments on it by A. Sekey, Detail detection in television signals, *ibid.* **53**, 75–76 (January 1965).

CHAPTER 7

Picture Properties and Pictorial Pattern Recognition

7.1. Pattern Recognition

As indicated in Section 1.2, one of the central problems in the field of picture processing by computer is that of *describing* pictures. In general a description of a picture might consist of a set of true statements about the picture in some appropriate language; we shall consider this general case in Chapter 10. Often, however, one only needs to *classify* the picture into one of a set of (usually prespecified) categories. For example, for a picture that shows a single printed character, the categories might be "A," ..., "Z"; for a picture showing a single type of cloud cover, the categories might be "cirrus," "cumulus," etc.

The general problem of automatic pattern classification is that of finding a function that maps the set of patterns (here, pictures) into the set of classes. It is usually convenient to do this in several steps:

1. *Preprocessing.* The given picture f is transformed ("preprocessed") into one or more new pictures $f_1, \ldots, f_k$, by performing a set of operations, or sequences of operations, on it.

2. *Feature extraction.* "Property" (or "feature") functions $\mathfrak{F}_1, \ldots, \mathfrak{F}_m$, which take pictures into real numbers, are applied to the f_i's. (It is sometimes advantageous to make this a two-step process in which pictures are first mapped into functions of a single variable, and the functions are, in turn, mapped into real numbers.)

3. *Classification.* The result of Steps 1 and 2 is an n-tuple ($n \leq mk$) of real numbers, which can be regarded as properties of the original picture f; we can think of such an n-tuple as a point in n-dimensional space. If the classes are specified as occupying given regions in this space, or as having given probability densities over this space, one can then assign the given picture to the

closest or most probable class. (The difficulty, in practice, is that the regions, or probabilities, are usually not known.)

There is an extensive literature on classification on the basis of a given set of properties (Step 3); since this is not a problem specific to picture processing, we shall not discuss it further .The basic idea in Step 1 is to preprocess in such a way as to make it easier, at Step 2, to extract features that are "good" in the sense that they, in turn, make classification easier, or make better classification possible. The techniques available for Step 1 have been treated in Chapters 4–6. In this and the next two chapters we deal with Step 2; specifically, we review the types of property functions that have been found useful in various pictorial pattern recognition tasks.

In discussing picture properties it is convenient to distinguish between properties that have natural definitions for an arbitrary picture, and those that have such definitions only if a special subset of the picture (an "object") has been singled out. For example, it is pointless to speak about such properties as the size and shape of a picture, since we usually deal only with pictures that are nonzero on a standard-sized square; however, one is very often interested in the sizes and shapes of various objects in a picture. Methods of singling out objects from pictures ("segmentation") will be considered in Chapter 8, and geometrical properties of picture subsets will be discussed in Chapter 9; in this chapter we shall be primarily concerned with properties that have natural definitions even if no subset of the picture is specified.

GENERAL REFERENCES†

Character Recognition

See OCR, as well as the first ten papers in PR², especially J. Rabinow, The present state of the art of reading machines, pp. 3–29.

1. National Science Foundation, "Current Research and Development in Scientific Documentation" [e.g., No. 14, NSF-66-17 (1966)]. U.S. Government Printing Office, Washington, D.C.
2. M. E. Stevens, Automatic character recognition—a state-of-the-art report, *Nat. Bur. Standards Tech. Note 112* (PB 161613) (May 1961).
3. L. M. Avrukh, A. M. Vasilyev, G. I. Sayenko, and L. M. Sindilevich, eds., "Reading Devices." Inst. of Sci. Inform. of Acad. of Sci., USSR, Moscow, 1962; available in translation as AD 401612 (March 1963).

† See also Section 1.3.

4. H. Freiberger and E. F. Murphy, Reading devices for the blind: an overview, "Human Factors in Technology" (E. M. Bennett, J. Degan, and J. Spiegel, eds.), pp. 299–314. McGraw-Hill, New York, 1963; (an earlier version is in *IRE Trans. Human Factors in Electronics* **HFE-2**, 8–19 (March 1961).

> See also H. Freiberger and E. F. Murphy, Reading machines for the blind, *Science* **152**, 679–680 (April 29, 1966).

5. W. J. Bijleveld, "Automatic Reading of Digits." Netherlands Automatic Inform. Process. Res. Ctr., Amsterdam, 1963.
6. N. Lindgren, Machine recognition of human language, Part III, Cursive script recognition, *IEEE Spectrum* **2**(5), 104–116 (May 1965).

> Much of this work has made use of real-time information (sequences of strokes, velocities, accelerations, etc.); since this is not "picture processing," it will not be reviewed here.

7. L. A. Feidelman, A survey of the character recognition field, *Datamation* **12**(2), 45–52 (February 1966).
8. R. A. Wilson, "Optical Page Reading Devices." Reinhold, New York, 1966.
9. Document Handling and Character Recognition Committee (1966), "Character Recognition." Brit. Comput. Soc., London, 1967.
10. V. A. Kovalevsky, "Character Readers and Pattern Recognition." Spartan, New York, 1968.

Other Applications†

11. W. T. Welford, Bubble chamber optics, *Appl. Opt.* **2**, 981–996 (October 1963).
12. H. Gelernter, Data collection and reduction for nuclear particle trace detectors, *Advances Comput.* **6**, 229–296 (1965).
13. Purdue Conference on Instrumentation for High-Energy Physics, *IEEE Trans. Nuclear Science* **NS-12** (August 1965).
14. B. Alder, S. Fernbach, and M. Rotenberg, eds., "Methods in Computational Physics," Vol. 5. Academic Press, New York, 1966.
15. R. N. Colwell, The extraction of data from aerial photographs by human and mechanical means, *Photogrammetria* **20**, 211–228 (1965).
16. S. F. Smillie, Automatic target recognition: some considerations, *IEEE Trans. Aerospace Electronic Systems* **AES-2**, 187–191 (March 1966).
17. S. A. Yefsky, ed., "Law Enforcement Science and Technology," pp. 445–515. Thompson, Washington, D.C., 1967 (ten papers on automatic fingerprint classification and recognition).
18. W. E. Tolles, ed., Data extraction and processing of optical images in the medical and biological sciences, *Ann. N. Y. Acad. Sci.* **157**, 1-530 (March 1969).

† See also PPR.

Related Subjects

19. V. S. Fain, Automatic recognition of patterns (report on the First All Union Symposium on Automatic Pattern Recognition. Moscow, June 1965), *Vestn. Akad. Nauk SSSR* **35**(10), 127–129 (1965); English translation: AD 665708 (June 1967).
20. M. S. Watanabe, ed., "Methodologies of Pattern Recognition." Academic Press, New York, in press, 1969.
21. P. A. Kolers and M. Eden, eds., "Recognizing Patterns: Studies in Living and Automatic Systems." M.I.T. Press, Cambridge, Massachusetts, 1968.
22. G. Nagy, State of the art in pattern recognition, *Proc. IEEE* **56**, 836–862 (May 1968).

7.2. Property Selection

Given a set of properties, it is, in principle, possible to compute the degree to which each property contributes to the classification decision [1–6], e.g., in terms of the average amount of information that is conveyed about the class membership of a pattern when the value of each property is specified. If this computation is impractical, one can still evaluate the effectivenesses of the properties empirically by implementing, or simulating, the recognition system (e.g., [7–13]; compare [14]). Many pattern recognition systems are able to modify the properties that they use in an attempt to find more effective ones (e.g., [15–18]; there are other types of "training" pattern recognition systems that modify not the properties themselves, but the weights given to them in making the classification decision). Since these approaches are not specific to pictorial patterns, they will not be considered here.

Of greater relevance to *pictorial* pattern recognition is the problem of selecting a "good" set of properties in the first place. In many proposed pattern recognition systems, the properties seem to have been selected because of their mathematical tractability (e.g., linearity, randomness, etc.) or ease of implementation (e.g., computability by optical means), rather than because of their suitability for the given classification task. In other cases properties (and preprocessing operations) have been designed in an attempt to simulate the physiology of the visual pathway. or to model visual perception. (See BPSS, PR, and MPSVF, as well as [19, 20]; specific examples are the Laplacian and "edge-detector" operations described in Section 6.5.) This approach can be rationalized on the grounds that the pattern classes often have no simple definitions, and that the only basis for assuming that the classification problem has a solution at all is the fact that the patterns can be correctly

classified by humans (or animals). On the other hand, many pattern classification problems have simple solutions based on preprocessing operations
(e.g., taking the Fourier transform) or property functions that almost certainly
bear no resemblance to those used by organisms.

The soundest approach to property selection is to use knowledge about
the "structure" of the patterns and the definitions of the classes as a guide
in choosing the properties and preprocessing operations. For example, if the
patterns are "line–drawing-like" (e.g., handwriting and hand printing,
nuclear bubble chamber pictures, etc.), certain types of properties and operations are evidently more appropriate than others. Even partial structural
descriptions of the classes (letters tend to consist of certain basic "strokes,"
etc.) can be very helpful, since the recognition system can be designed to look
for particular "local" patterns, for "figures" with particular shapes, etc.
The various "picture grammers" now under development (see Chapter 10)
provide formalisms in which a variety of pattern and class descriptions can
be expressed; but this work to date has had only limited applications.

Although there is as yet no general theory that can tell us how to define
"optimum" properties when given the definitions of the classes, there are
some special cases in which the optimum is known. For example, suppose
that all the patterns belonging to a given class can be obtained by adding
noise to an ideal ("prototype") pattern. In this case, as indicated in Section
6.1, the "template match" with the prototype is an optimum property.
More generally ([21, 22]; compare [23, 24]), it is possible to treat the case in
which there exists a set of prototype "subpatterns" such that each pattern is
a union of some of the subpatterns (plus noise).

In many cases two patterns must belong to the same class if they differ
only in position, orientation, size, etc., or if they can be obtained from one
another by a simple point operation such as a linear transformation of the
gray scale, etc. (This is not always the case; e.g., a comma and an apostrophe
may differ only in position, a "d" and a "p" only in orientation, and so on.)
In other words, in many cases the classes are *invariant* under certain types of
transformations (translation, rotation, magnification, gamma correction,
etc.). This constitutes a partial description of the classes and suggests the use
of properties that are invariant under the same transformations. In the following paragraphs we consider methods of defining invariant properties.

1. In some cases it is not impractical to actually apply all of the transformations to each given pattern, either one after the other or in parallel,

and to compute property values for each of the transformed patterns. For example, when we cross correlate a template with a picture, we are computing the "match" of the template with the picture in every possible position. This, of course, yields a very large set of property values, but one can obtain invariant properties from this set by taking its average, its maximum, etc.

2. If the set of transformations has a simple mathematical description, one can often define invariant properties mathematically. (In fact the various branches of geometry can be thought of as being concerned with those properties of figures that are invariant under various groups of transformations.) For example, the distances between points of a figure are invariant under translation and rotation, and their ratios are also invariant under magnification; thus, these distances (ratios) can be used as properties by which to assign the figure to a class of congruent (similar) figures. For less trivial examples, see the references on "moment invariants" in Section 7.3, as well as [25].

3. It is often possible to define a procedure for "normalizing" patterns, such that two patterns that differ by a transformation in the given set will become identical when they are normalized. Thus, any property of the normalized pattern is a transformation-invariant property of the original pattern. In the following paragraphs, we give three examples.

a. A pattern can be translated so that its centroid is at the origin of the coordinate system. (Here we are regarding the gray level at a point as representing the "mass" of the point.) Similarly, a pattern can be standardized in orientation, e.g., by finding the line through its centroid about which its moment of inertia is least, and then rotating the pattern to make this line one of the coordinate axes; note, however, that this minimum-inertia line may not be unique. [The eye can be thought of as performing a certain degree of normalization when it "fixates" (i.e., "centers") a figure, or adapts to over-all differences in brightness.]

b. As shown in Chapter 4, the autocorrelation and power spectrum of a picture are invariant under translation of the picture. Thus, template matching of autocorrelations, or of power spectra, provides a translation-invariant method of detecting a given pattern [26, 27]. Similarly, particular values of the autocorrelation, corresponding to particular shifts of the given picture relative to itself, provide a class of translation-invariant properties [28]. [There is evidence (e.g., [29, 30]) that the eyes of certain insects compute the autocorrelation of the visual field.]

It should be pointed out that specifying the autocorrelation does not determine the original picture "up to translation"; two functions can have the same autocorrelation even if they do not merely differ by a translation. For example, if g is obtained from f by a rotation through $180°$ [i.e., if $g(x, y) = f(-x, -y)$], we have $g \otimes g = \iint f(-x + u, -y + v)f(-x, -y) \, dx \, dy = \iint f(-x + u, -y + v)f(-x, -y) \, d(-x) \, d(-y) = f \otimes f.$ [Another trivial case: If the functions are not required to be nonnegative, we evidently have $(-f) \otimes (-f) = f \otimes f.$] As a nontrivial example, let $f = (a_{ij})$ and $g = (b_{ij})$ be the digital picture functions for which $a_{11} = 9$, $a_{12} = 6$, $a_{13} = 1$, $b_{11} = b_{13} = 3$, $b_{12} = 10$, and all other a's and b's are zero; then it is readily verified that $f \otimes f = g \otimes g$.

EXERCISE 1. Generalize the example just given as follows: Let $f = (a_{ij})$ be such that every a_{ij}, except possibly a_{11}, a_{12}, and a_{13}, is zero; then $f \otimes f$ is unchanged if we replace these three elements by $\frac{1}{2}[a_{12} + (a_{12}^2 - 4a_{11} a_{13})^{1/2}]$, $a_{11} + a_{13}$, and $\frac{1}{2}[a_{12} - (a_{12}^2 - 4a_{11} a_{13})^{1/2}]$, respectively.

★EXERCISE 2. Let f be as in Exercise 1. Show that the only changes in a_{11}, a_{12}, and a_{13} that leave $f \otimes f$ unchanged are those obtained by performing combinations of the following operations: (a) the one described in Exercise 1, (b) interchanging a_{11} and a_{13}, and (c) changing the signs of the a_{ij}'s. Generalize to an f in which $k \geq 3$ elements may be nonzero.

EXERCISE 3. Let $f = (a_{ij})$ and $g = (b_{ij})$ each have at most two elements different from zero. Show that we cannot have $f \otimes f = g \otimes g$ unless g can be obtained from f by a combination of translation, rotation through $180°$, and sign change. In other words, show that if the two elements in f are a_{rs} and a_{uv}, then the two elements in g are $b_{r+h, s+k}$ and $b_{u+h, v+k}$ for some h, k; and furthermore, we have either $a_{rs} = \pm b_{r+h, s+k}$, $a_{uv} = \pm b_{u+h, v+k}$, or vice versa.

It can be shown [31], however, that if two functions have the same autocorrelations of *all orders*, as defined by

$$\iint f(u, v)f(u + x_1, v + y_1) \cdots f(u + x_k, v + y_k) \, du \, dv \qquad (k = 1, 2, \ldots)$$

then they do, in fact, differ only by a translation. Indeed [32], for functions that are "discrete," or whose Fourier transforms are analytic, equality of the autocorrelations of the second (or any even) order ensures that the functions differ only by a translation.

One can obtain rotation invariance by analogous means. Since a picture $f(r, \theta)$ expressed in polar coordinates is periodic in θ with period 2π, the modulus of its Fourier series expansion (for each r) is rotation-invariant. A transform that is invariant under both rotation and magnification of the original picture can be obtained [33] by computing the "autocorrelation" in polar coordinates defined by

$$g(u, v) = \int_0^{2\pi} \int_0^{\infty} f(r, \theta) f(ur, \theta + v) r \, dr \, d\theta.$$

The transform is evidently unaffected by rotation of f, while magnification only multiplies it by a constant factor, which can be eliminated, e.g., by using a ratio of g's. If this operation is performed on the autocorrelation of f rather than on f itself, it yields a transform that is also translation-invariant. Alternatively [34], one can use a polar-coordinate version of the power spectrum to convert rotations and scale changes of the original picture into translations. On still another method of achieving scale invariance, see [32].

c. If the transformations are linear and form a group under composition of functions, a pattern can be converted into an invariant form by applying all the transformations to it and taking the sum (or the average) of the resulting patterns. For example, if one took a time-exposure photograph while rotating a pattern, the result would be a rotationally symmetric pattern that would not depend on the orientation of the original pattern. Evidently, this normalized pattern does not determine the original pattern "up to rotation." On the suggestion that the brain may construct invariants in this way, see [35, 36]; for some related work, see [37–41].

REFERENCES

1. P. M. Lewis, II, The characteristic selection problem in recognition systems, *IRE Trans. Information Theory* **IT-8**, 171–178 (February 1962).
2. T. Marill and D. M. Green, On the effectiveness of receptors in recognition systems, *ibid*. **IT-9**, 11–17 (January 1963).
3. J. T. Tou and R. P. Heydorn, Some approaches to optimum feature extraction, "Computer and Information Sciences, II" (J. T. Tou, ed.), pp. 57–89. Academic Press, New York, 1967.
4. M. S. Watanabe, P. F. Lambert, C. A. Kulikowski, J. L. Buxton, and R. Walker, Evaluation and selection of variables in pattern recognition, *ibid*., pp. 91–122.
5. C. W. Swonger, Property learning in pattern recognition systems using information content measurements, PR², pp. 329–347.
6. Y. T. Chien and K. S. Fu, Selection and ordering of feature observations in a pattern recognition system, *Information and Control* **12**, 395–414 (May–June 1968).

7. E. C. Greanias, C. J. Hoppel, M. Kloomok, and J. S. Osborne, Design of logic for recognition of printed characters by simulation, *IBM J. Res. Develop.* **1**, 8–18 (January 1957).

8. R. J. Evey, Use of a computer to design character recognition logic, *EJCC* pp. 205–211 (December 1959).

9. S. D. Stearns, A method for the design of pattern recognition logic, *IRE Trans. Electronic Computers* **EC-9**, 48–53 (March 1960).

10. D. N. Freeman, Computer synthesis of character recognition systems, *ibid.* **EC-10**, 735–747 (December 1961).

11. L. A. Kamentsky and C. N. Liu, Computer-automated design of multifont print recognition logic, *IBM J. Res. Develop.* **7**, 2–13 (January 1963).

12. C. N. Liu, A programmed algorithm for designing multifont character recognition logics, *IEEE Trans. Electronic Computers* **EC-13**, 586–593 (October 1964).

13. C. N. Liu and G. L. Shelton, Jr., An experimental investigation of a mixed-font print recognition system, *ibid.* **EC-15**, 916–925 (December 1966).

14. L. Uhr, Feature discovery and pattern description, PR^2, pp. 159–181.

15. B. Widrow, Generalization and information storage in networks of ADALINE "neurons," "Self-Organizing Systems 1962" (M. C. Yovits, G. T. Jacobi, and G. D. Goldstein, eds.), pp. 435–461. Spartan, New York, 1962.

16. L. Uhr and C. Vossler, A pattern-recognition program that generates, evaluates and adjusts its own operators, *WJCC* pp. 555–569 (May 1961); reprinted in PR, pp. 349–364.

17. R. D. Joseph, P. M. Kelly, and S. S. Viglione, An optical decision filter, *Proc. IEEE* **51**, 1098–1118 (August 1963).

18. R. D. Joseph and S. S. Viglione, A pattern recognition technique and its application to high resolution imagery, *SJCC* pp. 457–475 (April 1966).

19. L. Uhr, "Pattern recognition" computers as models for form perception, *Psychol. Bull.* **60**, 40–73 (January 1963).

20. N. S. Sutherland, "The Methods and Findings of Experiments on the Visual Discrimination of Shape by Animals," Exptl. Psychol. Soc. Monograph 1. Heffer's, Cambridge, 1961.

21. H. D. Block, N. J. Nilsson, and R. O. Duda, Determination and detection of features in patterns, "Computer and Information Sciences" (J. T. Tou and R. H. Wilcox, eds.), pp. 75–110. Spartan, New York, 1964.

22. U. Grenander, Toward a theory of patterns, *Symp. Probability Methods Analysis* pp. 79–111. Springer, Berlin, 1967.

23. J. R. Ullman, A simplification of the problem of choosing features, CPR, pp. 197–206.

24. J. M. Richardson, A rational approach to semi-adaptive pattern recognition, *ibid.*, pp. 220–227.

25. R. F. Meyer, V. E. Giuliano, and P. E. Jones, Analytic approximation and translational invariance in character recognition, OCR, pp. 181–195.

26. L. P. Horwitz and G. L. Shelton, Jr., Pattern recognition using autocorrelation, *Proc. IRE* **49**, 175–185 (January 1961).

27. J. D. Armitage and A. W. Lohmann, Character recognition by incoherent spatial filtering, *Appl. Opt.* **4**, 461–467 (April 1965); see also the comments, *ibid.* **4**, 1666 (December 1965).

28. R. Y. Kain, Autocorrelation pattern recognition, *Proc. IRE* **49**, 1085–1086 (June 1961).

29. W. Reichardt, Autocorrelation, a principle for the evaluation of sensory information by the central nervous system, "Sensory Communication" (W. Rosenblith, ed.), pp. 303–317. M.I.T. Press, Cambridge, Massachusetts, 1961; (reprinted in PR, pp. 212–223).
30. J. C. Bliss, Visual information processing in the beetle *Lixus*, OPI, pp. 124–144.
31. R. L. Adler and A. G. Konheim, A note on translation invariants, *Proc. Amer. Math. Soc.* **13**, 425–428 (June 1962).
32. J. A. McLaughlin and J. Raviv, *N*th-order autocorrelations in pattern recognition, *Information and Control* **12**, 121–142 (February 1968).
33. W. Doyle, Operations useful for similarity-invariant pattern recognition, *J. ACM* **9**, 259–267 (April 1962).
34. J. K. Brousil and D. R. Smith, A threshold logic network for shape invariance, *IEEE Trans. Electronic Computers* **EC-16**, 818–828 (December 1967).
35. W. Pitts and W. S. McCulloch, How we know universals—the perception of auditory and visual forms, *Bull. Math. Biophys.* **9**, 127–147 (1947).
36. D. M. MacKay, Some experiments on the perception of patterns modulated at the alpha frequency, *Electroencephalog. Clin. Neurophysiol.* **5**, 559–562 (1953).
37. F. Rosenblatt, Perceptual generalization over transformation groups, "Self-Organizing Systems" (M. C. Yovits and S. Cameron, eds.), pp. 63–100. Pergamon Press, New York, 1960.
38. J. R. Singer, Electronic analog of the human recognition system, *J. Opt. Soc. Amer.* **51**, 61–69 (January 1961).
39. J. R. Singer, A self organizing recognition system, *WJCC* pp. 545–554 (May 1961).
40. M. Kabrisky, "A Proposed Model for Visual Information Processing in the Human Brain." Univ. of Illinois Press, Chicago, Illinois, 1966.
41. W. C. Hoffman, The Lie algebra of visual perception, *J. Math. Psychol.* **3**, 65–98 (1966); and errata, *ibid.* **4**, 348–349 (1967).

7.3. Classes of Properties

Only a few of the many possible types of picture properties have been used for pattern recognition purposes. In this section we discuss some of the important classes of such properties. By a property of a picture, we mean here a real number, which is the result of applying some function to the picture; in the next section we shall discuss function-valued "properties."

An important case is that of a binary-valued property, which can only have the values 0 and 1; such as property can be regarded as a *predicate* that is either true or false for a given picture. (Given any real-valued property $\mathfrak{F}$, one can define binary-valued properties $\mathfrak{F}_t$ by "thresholding" $\mathfrak{F}$, i.e., by defining $\mathfrak{F}_t = 1$ if $\mathfrak{F} \geq t$, $\mathfrak{F}_t = 0$ otherwise, where t is a real number.) In the case of a binary-valued digital picture, a binary-valued property is simply a *Boolean function* of a finite number of arguments.

a. *Local Properties and Textural Properties*

The value of a property $\mathfrak{F}(f)$ need not depend on the entire set of values of f, but only on a subset of these values—in other words, on the values of f restricted to a subset of the plane. If we regard our picture functions as being defined on a finite set A (e.g., if they are digital), there evidently exists a smallest subset B of A such that $\mathfrak{F}(f)$ depends, for all pictures f, only on the restriction of f to B. This B is called the *set of support* of $\mathfrak{F}$. We say that $\mathfrak{F}$ is *local* if the diameter of B, or the number of points in B, is small. For example, if ϕ is a local operation (Section 4.1), the value of $\phi(f)$ at any point is a local property of f, since it depends only on the gray levels in a neighborhood of the point. The extreme case of a local property is a "point property," i.e., a function of the gray level of the picture at a specific point. [It can be shown (see [1–3]) that if there are just n possible patterns. they can be distinguished by using at most $n - 1$ point properties.]

Local properties are useful primarily in cases where the pictures in question can be normalized, since otherwise they will, in general, have totally different values for pictures that differ only by, say, a translation. For examples of local properties applied to the recognition of characters that have been normalized in position, see [4–6]. On the use of local properties of the power spectrum of a picture, see [7, 8]. To make a local property somewhat insensitive to position, one can blur the picture slightly before measuring the property [9].

EXERCISE 1. Find a set of point properties of the autocorrelation that can be used to distinguish the six patterns of Exercise 1, Section 6.1, independent of their positions.

Even in an unnormalized picture, one can obtain invariant properties by analyzing the *frequency distribution* of the values of any local property over the picture. For example, the statistics of this distribution, such as its average, or the fraction of the picture area over which it has a given range of values, are invariant. We shall call statistics of local properties *textural properties*. Properties of this type have been used for such purposes as the automatic classification of terrain or cloud-cover types from aerial or satellite photographs ([10–16]; compare [17]).

★EXERCISE 2. In the random digital picture of Exercise 2, Section 6.1, compute the averages of the following local properties as functions of p: (a) the gray level itself, (b) the gradient, and (c) the Laplacian.

> The importance of "visual texture" in pattern perception has been stressed by Gibson [18]; by "texture," he seems to mean the average size of the elements of which a pattern is composed. Note that this size is inversely related to the number of edges per unit area (see [19]), which, for pictures of a given sharpness, can be regarded as the average value of a local property (e.g., of the gradient or Laplacian). A number of investigators have proposed measures of texture similar to those used to measure photographic granularity (Section 6.3). Other investigators [20, 21] have studied texture measures based on the conditional probability distribution of the gray level of a picture element, given the gray levels of one or more "preceding" elements.

b. Linear Properties

Just as (Section 4.2) any position-invariant linear operation is a convolution, so we can show that any linear property that satisfies a certain boundedness condition is a "template match," i.e., it is the integral (over the plane) of the product of some "template" function and the given picture. Specifically, let $\mathscr{S}$ be the set of all real-valued functions of two real variables that are defined and integrable over the plane, and for which $\int_{-\infty}^{\infty}\int_{-\infty}^{\infty}f^2$ is finite. Then we have

THEOREM. Let $\mathfrak{F}$ be a real-valued linear function defined on $\mathscr{S}$ and suppose that there exists a real number M such that, for all f in $\mathscr{S}$, we have $\mathfrak{F}(f) \leq M(\iint f^2)^{1/2}$. Then there exists some g in $\mathscr{S}$ such that $\mathfrak{F}(f) = \iint gf$ for all f in $\mathscr{S}$.

PROOF. Let M^* be the least M for which the hypothesis of the theorem holds, and let g^* be such that $\mathfrak{F}(g^*) = M^*(\iint g^{*2})^{1/2}$, where $\iint g^{*2} = 0$.

> The fact that such an M^* and g^* exist follows from the "completeness" of the set $\mathscr{S}$. Our theorem is known as the Riesz representation theorem; see, e.g., P. R. Halmos, "Introduction to Hilbert Space

and the Theory of Spectral Multiplicity," pp. 31–32. Chelsea, New York, 1957.

Let h be such that $\mathfrak{F}(h) = 0$; then, for any real λ, we have $M^{*^2} \iint g^{*^2} = \mathfrak{F}(g^*)^2 = \mathfrak{F}(g^* - \lambda h)^2 \leq M^{*^2} \iint (g^* - \lambda h)^2 = M^{*^2}(\iint g^{*^2} - 2\lambda \iint g^* h + \lambda^2 \iint h^2)$, so that $0 \leq \lambda^2 \iint h^2 - 2\lambda \iint g^* h$. If $\iint h^2 \neq 0$, let $\lambda = \iint g^* h / \iint h^2$; then we have $0 \leq -(\iint g^* h)^2$, so that $\iint g^* h = 0$. On the other hand, if $\iint h^2 = 0$, we have $0 \leq \iint g^* h \leq (\iint g^{*^2} \iint h^2)^{1/2} = 0$ by the Schwarz inequality; thus, we have shown that $\iint g^* h = 0$, for any h such that $\mathfrak{F}(h) = 0$. But, for any f, we can write $f = [f - \mathfrak{F}(f)g^*/M^*(\iint g^{*^2})^{1/2}] + \mathfrak{F}(f)g^*/M^*(\iint g^{*^2})^{1/2}$, where $\mathfrak{F}$ takes the expression in brackets into 0. Hence, multiplying both sides by g^* and integrating, we have $\iint g^* f = \mathfrak{F}(f) \iint g^{*^2}/M^*(\iint g^{*^2})^{1/2}$, so that $\mathfrak{F}(f) = M^* \iint g^* f/(\iint g^{*^2})^{1/2}$; and we can take $g = M^* g^*/(\iint g^{*^2})^{1/2}$ to prove the theorem. ∎

Template match properties are particularly applicable to cases where the patterns can be normalized; they have been used extensively in character recognition systems (see the general references cited in Section 7.1). If the patterns to be classified are highly standardized, e.g., if they are star patterns or characters from a specific type font, it becomes practical to use templates of complete patterns as properties; in this case one can simply classify an unknown pattern as being the same as the template that it best matches. (On the star pattern recognition literature, see [1], Section 6.1.) Another important class of linear properties is that in which the templates are mathematically simple functions, e.g., polynomials, sinusoids, etc.

One can construct a set of mutually "independent" properties of this type by using a set of orthogonal functions as templates. For example, the Fourier coefficients of a picture function are such a set of properties.

For example, if the functions are the monomials $x^i y^j$, we obtain the *moments* [22–30] of the given picture function; here, a natural way of normalizing is to take the origin at the centroid (so that the moments become "central moments").

EXERCISE 3. Compute the central moments of the six patterns in Exercise 1 for all i, j, such that $i + j \leq 2$. Which of these moments could best be used as properties to distinguish among the patterns?

c. *Properties Linear with Respect to a Given Set of Properties*†

The property $\mathfrak{G}$ is said to be linear with respect to the set of properties $\mathfrak{S}$ if $\mathfrak{G} = \sum_{\mathfrak{S}} a_{\mathfrak{F}} \mathfrak{F}$, where the a's are real numbers. Similarly, if $\mathfrak{G}$ is binary-valued, we say that it is a linear threshold property with respect to $\mathfrak{S}$ if there exist real numbers $a_{\mathfrak{F}}$ and a real number t such that $\mathfrak{G} = 1$ if and only if $\sum_{\mathfrak{S}} a_{\mathfrak{F}} \mathfrak{F} \geq t$.

In what follows we assume that all picture functions are binary-valued and are defined on a finite set A. The binary-valued property $\mathfrak{F}$ is called a *mask* if there exists a region S in A such that $\mathfrak{F}(f) = 1$ if and only if $f = 1$ at every point of S. [Note that this is equivalent to $\mathfrak{F}(f) = \prod_{x \in S} f(x)$.]

> PROPOSITION. Any binary-valued property is a linear threshold property with respect to the set of all masks.

> PROOF. Let $\mathfrak{G}$ be a binary-valued function of the binary-valued variables $y_1, \ldots, y_n$ (which are the values of f at the n points of A). Then $\mathfrak{G}$ can be written in "normal form" as a disjunction of conjunctions of which each term is a y_i or a $\bar{y}_i$; and since only one of the conjunctions can be 1 for any given f, their disjunction is the same as their sum. If we replace each $\bar{y}_i$ in each conjunction by $1 - y_i$, multiply out, and group like terms, we thus obtain an expression for $\mathfrak{G}$ as a linear combination of products of y's with integer coefficients. ∎

By the *order* of $\mathfrak{G}$, we mean the smallest k for which there exists an $\mathfrak{S}$ such that $\mathfrak{G}$ is a linear threshold property with respect to $\mathfrak{S}$, and the set of support of every $\mathfrak{F}$ in $\mathfrak{S}$ has at most k elements. For example:

1. $\mathfrak{G}$ has order 0 if and only if it is constant.
2. Any mask has order 1. In fact, given any region S in A, the mask defined by S is 1 if and only if $\sum_{x \in S} \mathfrak{F}_x \geq |S|$ (the number of elements of A in S), where $\mathfrak{F}_x$ is the mask defined by $\{x\}$ (so that $\mathfrak{F}_x$ has a one-element set of support).
3. It can be shown that if $\mathfrak{G}$ and $\mathfrak{H}$ have orders r and s, respectively, then $\mathfrak{G} + \mathfrak{H} - 2\mathfrak{G}\mathfrak{H}$ ("$\mathfrak{G}$ or $\mathfrak{H}$ but not both") and $1 - (\mathfrak{G} - \mathfrak{H})^2$ ("$\mathfrak{G}$ if and only if $\mathfrak{H}$") have orders $\leq r + s$. Surprisingly, however, for any n, there exist $\mathfrak{G}$

† See [31].

and $\mathfrak{H}$, both of order 1, such that $\mathfrak{GH}$ (" $\mathfrak{G}$ and $\mathfrak{H}$ ") and $\mathfrak{G} + \mathfrak{H} - \mathfrak{GH}$ (" $\mathfrak{G}$ or $\mathfrak{H}$ ") have orders $> n$.

The following are some other interesting examples of orders of $\mathfrak{G}$'s that express properties of S_f (the set of elements at which $f = 1$):

4. " $|S_f|$ is odd " has order $|A|$.

5. " S_f is connected " has order that grows with $|A|$.

6. "The genus of S_f is $< m$ " has order ≤ 4 for any m (see Section 9.1 for the definition of genus and the proof.)

7. " S_f is convex " has order ≤ 3 (see Section 8.4b for the definition of convexity and the proof).

8. The only translation-invariant properties of order 1 are those of the form " $|S_f| < k$ " and " $|S_f| > k$ ".

One can also study properties that are linear threshold functions with respect to a set of properties whose sets of support have bounded diameters (rather than bounded numbers of elements). It is easily seen that " $|S_f| \leq k$ " is of diameter 1; but it is not difficult to show that " $|S_f| = k$ " has a diameter that increases with that of A, as does " S_f is connected."

Even if a property is a linear threshold function with respect to a given set of properties, the linearity may not be realizable in practice, since the coefficients required may have to span an impractically large range. For example, it can be shown that if " $|S_f|$ is odd " is expressed as a linear threshold function with respect to the set of all masks, the ratio of the largest to the smallest coefficient grows exponentially with $|A|$.

d. *Random Properties*

Many pattern recognition systems have employed properties that are defined by random processes. For example, a random linear property can be defined by generating a random function and using it as a template. In the "simple Perceptron" [32], each "A-unit" computes a different property of this type, where the random template functions can take on only the values 0, 1, and -1. (Moreover, the " R-unit " computes a linear threshold property with respect to the set of properties computed by the individual A-units.) For examples of other systems that use random properties, see [33–36].

EXERCISE 4. Design several 3-by-3 binary-valued random templates by tossing a coin, and compute their matches with the six patterns of Exercise 1.

One need not use properties that are completely random; they can be designed to satisfy various types of constraints. For example, one can use random templates that tend to be "clustered" [36, 37] or that are line-like "scribbles" ([38, 39]; compare [40]). One can also generate random functions "without replacement," so that the sets of support of the functions are all disjoint [41, 42].

REFERENCES

1. A. Glovazky, Determination of redundancies in a set of patterns, *IRE Trans. Information Theory* **IT-2**, 151–153 (December 1956).
2. A. Gill, Minimum-scan pattern recognition, *ibid.* **IT-5**, 52–57 (June 1959).
3. B. H. Mayoh, Optimal classification of objects, Algorithm 83, *Comm. ACM* **5**, 167–168 (March 1963).
4. J. S. Bomba, Alpha-numeric character recognition using local operations, *EJCC* pp. 218–224 (December 1959).
5. L. A. Kamentsky, The simulation of three machines which read rows of handwritten arabic numbers, *IRE Trans. Electronic Computers* **EC-10**, 489–501 (September 1961).
6. M. Fischler, R. L. Mattson, O. Firschein, and L. D. Healy, An approach to general pattern recognition, *IRE Trans. Information Theory* **IT-8**, S64–S73 (September 1962).
7. G. G. Lendaris and G. L. Stanley, An opticalogical self-organizing recognition system, OEOIP, pp. 535–550.
8. R. H. Asendorf, The remote reconnaissance of extraterrestrial environments, PPR, pp. 223–238.
9. D. O. Claydon, M. B. Clowes, and J. R. Parks, Letter recognition and the segmentation of running text, *Information and Control* **9**, 246–264 (June 1966).
10. A. Rosenfeld, Automatic recognition of basic terrain types from aerial photographs, *Photogrammetric Engrg.* **28**, 115–132 (March 1962).
11. A. Rosenfeld and A. Goldstein, Optical correlation for terrain type discrimination, *ibid.* **30**, 639–646 (June 1964).
12. D. Steiner and H. Haefner, Tone distortion for automated interpretation, *ibid.* **31**, 269–280 (March 1965).
13. J. K. Hawkins, G. T. Elerding, K. W. Bixby, and P. A. Haworth, Automatic shape detection for programmed terrain classification, "Filmed Data and Computers," Paper No. XVI. Soc. Photo-Opt. Instr. Engrs., Redondo Beach, California, June 1966.
14. J. K. Hawkins and G. T. Elerding, Image feature extraction for automatic terrain classification, "Computerized Imaging Techniques," Paper No. VI. Soc. Photo-Opt. Instr. Engrs., Redondo Beach, California, June 1967.
15. E. M. Darling, Jr. and R. D. Joseph, Pattern recognition from satellite altitudes, *IEEE Trans. Systems Science and Cybernetics* **SSC-4**, 38–47 (March 1968).

16. E. M. Darling, Jr. and R. D. Joseph, An experimental investigation of video pattern recognition, PPR, pp. 457–469.

The Automatic Target Recognition Device described by W. Swoboda and J. W. Gerdes, in A system for demonstrating the effects of changing background on automatic target recognition, PPR, pp. 33–43 also makes use of a variety of textural properties.

17. J. M. S. Prewitt and M. L. Mendelsohn, The analysis of cell images, *Ann. New York Acad. Sci.* **128**, 1035–1053 (January 1966).
18. J. J. Gibson, "The Perception of the Visual World." Houghton, Boston, Massachusetts, 1950.
19. W. Carel, W. Purdy, and R. Lubow, The visilog: a bionic approach to visual space perception and orientation, *Proc. Nat. Aerospace Electron. Confer. (Dayton, Ohio)* pp. 295–300 (May, 1961).
20. B. Julesz, Visual pattern discrimination, *IRE Trans. Information Theory* **IT-8**, 84–92 (February 1962).
21. R. M. Pickett, The perception of a visual texture, *J. Exptl. Psychol.* **68**, 13–20 (1964).

For further work on visual texture perception, see B. Julesz, Some recent studies in vision relevant to form perception, MPSVF, pp. 136–154; A. Rosenfeld, On models for the perception of visual texture, *ibid.*, pp. 219–223; and R. M. Pickett, The perception of random visual texture, *ibid.*, pp. 224–232.

22. A. Shimbel, A logical program for the simulation of visual pattern recognition, "Principles of Self-Organization " (H. von Foerster and G. W. Zopf, Jr., eds.), pp. 521–526. Pergamon Press, New York, 1962.
23. M.-K. Hu, Pattern recognition by moment invariants, *Proc. IRE* **49**, 1428 (September 1961).
24. M.-K. Hu, A mathematical model for visual perception, BPSS, pp. 222–229.
25. M.-K. Hu, Visual pattern recognition by moment invariants, *IRE Trans. Information Theory* **IT-8**, 179–187 (February 1962).
26. V. E. Giuliano, P. E. Jones, R. F. Meyer, G. E. Kimball, and B. A. Stein, A Gestalt method of automatic pattern recognition, *Proc. 3rd Intern. Congr. Cybernetics (September 1961)* pp. 370–383. Association Internationale de Cybernétique, Namur, Belgium, 1965.
27. V. E. Giuliano, P. E. Jones, G. E. Kimball, R. F. Meyer, and B. A. Stein, Automatic pattern recognition by a Gestalt method, *Information and Control* **4**, 332–345 (December 1961).
28. F. L. Alt, Digital pattern recognition by moments, OCR, pp. 153–179; also published in *J. ACM* **9**, 240–258 (April 1962).
29. J. W. Butler, M. K. Butler, and A. Stroud, Automatic analysis of chromosomes, I, "Data Acquisition and Processing in Biology and Medicine," Vol. 3, pp 261–275. Pergamon Press, New York, 1963; Automatic analysis of chromosomes, II, *ibid.*, Vol. 4, pp. 47–57. Pergamon Press, New York, 1964.
30. S. Moskowitz, Terminal guidance by pattern recognition—a new approach, *IEEE Trans. Aerospace Navigational Electronics* **ANE-11**, 254–265 (December 1964).

31. M. L. Minsky and S. Papert, Linearly unrecognizable patterns, *Proc. Symp. Appl. Math.* **19**, 176–217. Amer. Math. Soc., Providence, Rhode Island, 1967.

   See also M. L. Minsky and S. Papert, "Perceptrons, an Introduction to Computational Geometry." M.I.T. Press, Cambridge, Massachusetts, 1969.

32. F. Rosenblatt, "Principles of Neurodynamics." Spartan, New York, 1962.

33. A. E. Murray, Perceptron applications in photo interpretation, *Photogrammetric Engrg.* **27**, 627–637 (September 1961).

34. W. S. Holmes, H. R. Leland, and J. L. Muerle, Recognition of mixed-font imperfect characters, OCR, pp. 213–225.

35. A. Borsellino and A. Gamba, An outline of a mathematical theory of PAPA, *Nuovo Cimento, Suppl.* **20**, 221–231 (1961).

36. L. G. Roberts, Pattern recognition with an adaptive network, *IRE Intern. Conv. Record* Part 2, pp. 66–70 (March 1960); reprinted in PR, pp. 295–300.

37. R. Bakis, N. M. Herbst, and G. Nagy, An experimental study of machine recognition of hand-printed numerals, *IEEE Trans. Systems Science and Cybernetics* **SSC-4**, 119–132 (July 1968).

38. A. Hoffman, The "whirling dervish," a simulation study in learning and recognition systems, *IRE Intern. Conv. Record* Part 4, pp. 153–160 (March 1962).

39. J. S. Bryan, Experiments in adaptive pattern recognition, *IEEE Trans. Military Electronics* **MIL-7**, 174–179 (April-July 1963).

40. F. Rosenblatt, A comparison of several Perceptron models, "Self-Organizing Systems 1962" (M. C. Yovits, G. T. Jacobi, and G. D. Goldstein, eds.), pp. 463–484. Spartan, New York, 1962.

41. W. W. Bledsoe and I. Browning, Pattern recognition and reading by machine, *EJCC* pp. 225–232 (December 1959); reprinted in PR, pp. 301–316.

42. G. P. Steck, Stochastic model for the Browning-Bledsoe pattern recognition scheme, *IRE Trans. Electronic Computers* **EC-11**, 274–282 (April 1962).

7.4. Functions of Pictures

As mentioned at the beginning of this chapter, it is sometimes useful to work with picture properties that are not real numbers, but real-valued *functions* of a single variable. [One could also consider properties that were functions of two (or more!) variables, but there would normally be no point in doing so, since such entities would be at least as hard to handle as the original picture. It should be noted, on the other hand, that even a property that is a single number may contain as much information as the original picture. For example, an n-by-n binary-valued picture is completely determined by specifying a single n^2-bit number, and similarly for gray-scale pictures. When we compute properties, it is because they make it easier for us to classify the picture, not because they necessarily involve a reduction in information content.] In this section we describe some useful classes of function-valued properties.

a. Frequency Distributions

As pointed out in Section 7.3a, one can compute the frequency distribution of the values of any local property over a picture; statistics of such distributions constitute useful textural properties.

★ EXERCISE 1. Compute the frequency distributions of the values of the gradient and Laplacian for the random picture.

b. Cross Sections

In many cases, sufficient information to perform a given pattern recognition task can be obtained from a picture by analyzing only a few "slices" of it. This approach is particularly applicable if the picture is first normalized to some extent. For example, in character recognition [1–3] one can take slices along the printed or written line at various heights; this yields a set of functions of the form $f(x, y_0)$. Cross sections at other orientations can also be useful [4]. Similarly, one can take cross sections of the autocorrelation of a picture. For example, consider a slice of $g = f \otimes f$ along a circle centered at the origin, i.e., a function of the form $g(r_0, \theta)$. This slice gives the values of $f \otimes f$ for a sequence of shifts in which f is "nutated," i.e., in which f revolves around the origin, without rotating, in an orbit of radius r_0 [5]. [On the generalization of this method to higher-order autocorrelations, see [6]; compare also [7], which proposes a method essentially equivalent to computing $g(r_0, \theta)$ for small r_0.]

EXERCISE 2. Plot $f \otimes f$, for each of the six patterns of Exercise 1, Section 6.1, around the square of radius 1, centered at the origin. Do these plots contain enough information to distinguish the patterns?

c. Functions Defined Using Families of Subsets

Let $\mathscr{A}$ be a one-parameter family of subsets A_λ of the plane, e.g., parallel lines, lines through a given point, concentric circles, etc. If we compute the value of some given picture property over just the set A_λ, we can regard the result as a function of λ. For example, we can compute the linear property

$\iint gf$ over A_λ by performing the integration over the set A_λ rather than over the entire plane; if A is a curve (as in all of the cases below), this integral becomes a "line integral" $\int_{A_\lambda} gf$ taken along the curve. In the following cases we take g to be the constant function 1.

1. If $\mathscr{A}$ is a family of parallel lines, e.g., the family $x = \lambda$, the integration can be thought of as "collapsing" f onto the x axis. A simple way of doing this is to move a thin vertical slit horizontally across the picture; the total amount of light that passes through the slit in a given position is approximately proportional to the integral of the picture function along the center line of the slit [8–10].

EXERCISE 3. Collapse the six patterns of Exercise 2 on the x axis; do the results contain enough information to distinguish the patterns? Do the same for the autocorrelations of the patterns.

[A process of "collapsing" onto the x and y axes is believed (e.g., [11]) to play a major role in the discrimination of visual patterns by the octopus.]

2. Let $\mathscr{A}$ be a family of concurrent lines, e.g., in polar coordinates the family $\theta = \lambda$. The resulting function can be used for the detection of radial edges or lines in the original picture, since their presence will produce high values in the derivative of the function. This function can be computed approximately by using a rotating slit, or equivalently, a "flying-line scanner" (i.e., a flying-spot scanner in which the "spot" is a long, thin streak that can be rotated to any orientation) [12, 13].

3. Let $\mathscr{A}$ be a family of concentric circles, e.g., in polar coordinates the family $r = \lambda$. A simple way of obtaining this function is to rotate an image of the picture (e.g., using rotating mirrors) and to integrate (over time) the light passing through a fixed radial slit in the image plane [14]. (A similar result can be obtained by reflecting the picture in a concave conical mirror.)

Just as for cross sections, one can compute a family of contour integrals (or more generally, a function defined using a family of subsets) on a pre-processed picture rather than on the original picture. On the case of the family of circles $r = \lambda$, using $f \otimes f$ rather than f itself, see [15, 16], as well as [33] in Section 7.2. For a binary-valued picture with set of 1's S_f, this function can be thought of as the probability that a randomly oriented line segment of length λ with one end in S_f also has its other end in S_f.

EXERCISE 4. Plot the sums of f and of $f \otimes f$, for the six patterns of Exercise 2, over the squares of radii 0, 1, 2, centered at the origin.

REFERENCES

1. T. L. Dimond, Devices for reading handwritten characters, *EJCC* pp. 232–237 (December 1957).
2. L. D. Harmon, Handwriting reader recognizes whole words, *Electronics* **35**, 29–31 (August 24, 1962).
3. L. D. Earnest, Machine recognition of cursive writing, "Information Processing 1962" (C. M. Popplewell, ed.), pp. 462–466. North-Holland, Amsterdam, 1963.
4. R. W. Weeks, Rotating raster character recognition system, *Trans. AIEE* **80**, Part I, 353–359 (September 1961).
5. M. B. Clowes and J. R. Parks, A new technique in automatic character recognition, *Comput. J.* **4**, 121–128 (July 1961).
6. M. B. Clowes, The use of multiple auto-correlation in character recognition, OCR, pp. 305–318.
7. D. N. Buell, Chrysler optical processing scanner, *EJCC* pp. 353–370 (December 1961).
8. C. C. Heasly, Jr., Some communication aspects of character-sensing systems, *WJCC* pp. 176–180 (March 1959).
9. W. E. Dickinson, A character-recognition study, *IBM J. Res. Develop.* **4**, 335–348 (July 1960).
10. W. T. Booth, G. M. Miller, and O. A. Schleich, Design considerations for stylized-font character readers, OCR, pp. 115–128.
11. J. Z. Young, "A Model of the Brain." Oxford Univ. Press, London and New York, 1964.
12. D. J. Innes, FILTER—a topological pattern separation computer program, *EJCC* pp. 25–37 (December 1960).
13. T. L. Watts, Scanning and measuring photographs of bubble chamber tracks using a computer controlled line segment ("PEPR"), PPR, pp. 207–220.
14. M. R. Uffelman, Target detection, prenormalization, and learning machines, *ibid.*, pp. 503–521.
15. G. Tenery, A pattern recognition function of integral geometry, *IEEE Trans. Military Electronics* **MIL-7**, 196–199 (April-July 1963).
16. G. R. Tenery, Information flow in a Bionics image recognition system, MPSVF, pp. 403–408.

CHAPTER 8

Picture Segmentation

Many pictorial pattern recognition problems involve more than just the assignment of a picture to one of a set of prespecified classes; they require a *description* of the picture, where the number of possible descriptions is so large that it makes it impractical to regard each description as defining a class. Typically, a description refers to various subsets of the picture ("objects") and specifies properties of these subsets. To arrive at such a description, an automatic pattern recognition system must be capable of singling out the appropriate picture subsets ("segmentation"). There is no universal method of segmenting a picture; many different types of subsets can be "objects," depending on the type of description that is required. In Section 8.1 we discuss methods of segmenting an arbitrary given picture, and in the remaining sections of this chapter we consider methods of defining new subsets in terms of a subset that has already been singled out.

8.1. Segmentation of an Arbitrary Picture

Specifying a subset of a picture is equivalent to specifying its "characteristic function," i.e., the function whose value is 1 at the points of the subset and 0 elsewhere. The basic method used for singling out a subset of a picture is to obtain the characteristic function of the subset by *thresholding* the given picture, or, more commonly, some picture derived from the given one by appropriate *preprocessing*. Specifically, for any picture f, any operation ϕ that takes pictures into pictures, and any real number t, we can take as a subset the set of points $S_{\phi, t}$ at which the transformed picture $\phi(f)$ has a gray level $\geq t$. [Alternatively, we can take the figure to be the set on which $\phi(f) \leq t, < t$, or $> t$; we can specify two thresholds $t_1 \leq t_2$ and take the set on which $t_1 \leq \phi(f) \leq t_2$; or even more generally, we can take the set on which $\phi(f)$ has a specified set of gray levels. These methods are not really more general than the simple thresholding of $\phi(f)$, since by combining ϕ with a suitable point operation, we can transform the gray scale so that the desired set of gray levels becomes $\geq t$ while all others become $< t$.] In the following paragraphs we give some important examples of this approach.

1. *Thresholding the picture itself.* Picture subsets can be defined by simply thresholding the gray levels in f itself; in other words, we can take ϕ to be the identity operation. In many cases this may be a very natural approach; e.g., in automatic character recognition the characters are "black" and the page "white"; in cloud pattern recognition, the clouds are "whiter" than most types of terrain. When we produced the binary-valued picture in Figure 3.1(e) by thresholding the original 32-level cloud-cover picture [Figure 3.1(a)], we were in effect singling out the clouds as a subset. If the picture f is a more or less continuous function, line-like or point-like subsets are often obtained when one takes the set of points whose gray levels are between two closely spaced thresholds (e.g., Figure 8.1); such figures are sometimes called "isophotes."

2. *Smoothing plus thresholding.* We can use ϕ to "smooth" or "clean up" the picture, e.g., by removing noise, so that the subset obtained by thresholding will not contain many "noise points." (On smoothing operations, see Section 6.4.) As an example of how this approach can be applied, consider a cloud-cover picture in which there are "overcast," "broken," and "clear" areas. If we smooth the picture by averaging it, and then threshold at a very high (low) value, we can single out the overcast (clear) area as one subset, and the remainder of the picture ("broken") as another [1]. For a refinement of this approach in another application, see [2].

3. *Sharpening plus thresholding.* We can take ϕ to be an operation that yields high values at edges and low values elsewhere. (On such "sharpening" operations, see Section 6.5.) Thresholding $\phi(f)$ will then tend to yield point-like or line-like subsets. This method can be used to single out subsets that cannot be characterized as having a prespecified range of gray levels, but that contrast with their immediate surroundings; it will yield "outlines" of such subsets. Note, however, that there is no guarantee that these outlines will be closed curves; if a contrasting region blurs into its surroundings at a given point, it may be impossible to extract an outline of the region that is not broken at that point. Direct thresholding of the gray levels in a picture, on the other hand, will single out an above-threshold region no matter how blurred it may be at its edges.

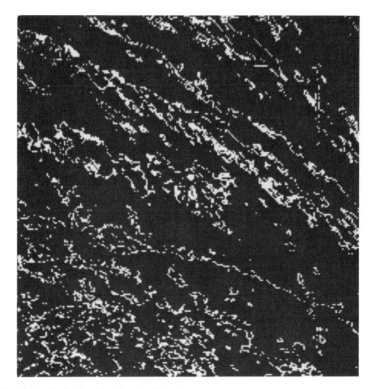

Figure 8.1. "Isophotes" obtained by thresholding the
32-level cloud-cover picture in Figure 3.1(a); gray levels
16–19 are shown as white, all other levels as black.

4. *Matched filtering plus thresholding.* If ϕ is a matched filtering operation, say the normalized cross correlation $\iint fg / (\iint f^2 \iint g^2)^{1/2}$ of f with a "template" pattern g (Section 6.1), then thresholding $\phi(f)$ will single out points where f matches g closely. Note that it will not yield the pattern g itself as a subset, but only a point or small region corresponding to the set of translations at which g matches well with f.

A crucial problem in using picture segmentation methods based on thresholding is that of how to select the threshold. In many cases it is not possible to do this in advance, since the correct threshold may not be the same for all pictures. However, it is sometimes possible to select a good threshold for each picture f automatically by examining the frequency distribution of gray levels in $\phi(f)$. The following are two examples of this approach.

129

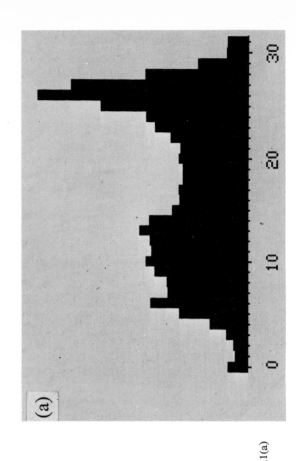

Figure 8.2. (a) Bar graph showing the number of elements in Figure 3.1(a) having each gray level, 0,..., 31. (b) Result of thresholding Figure 3.1(a) between 17 and 18 (levels 0–17 are shown as black, levels 18–31 as white), illustrating the *p*-tile method of threshold selection. (c) Result of thresholding Figure 3.1(a) between 18 and 19, illustrating the mode method.

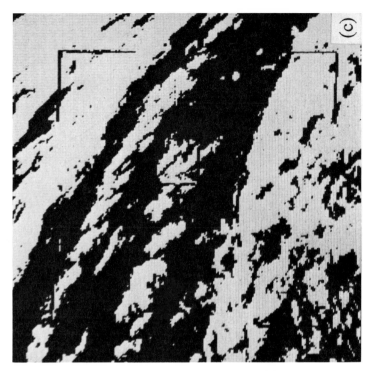

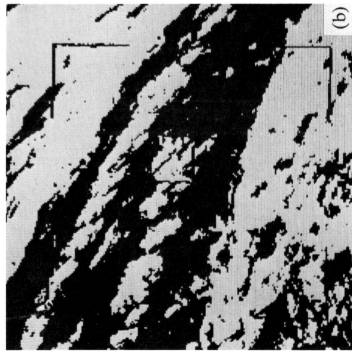

1. *The p-tile method.* If the approximate area of the desired subset is known (e.g., the characters occupy a certain proportion of the space on a printed page), one can use an appropriate *p*-tile of the distribution as a threshold; i.e., one can choose the lowest threshold *t* such that the area of the set at which $f(x, y) \geq t$ does not exceed a prespecified proportion of the area of the picture (see e.g., [33], Section 7.2).

2. *The mode method.* If the desired subset has a range of gray levels different from those that occur in the rest of the picture, the distribution may show a peak ("mode") corresponding to these levels, and one can segment the picture by choosing the thresholds at the bottoms of the valleys bordering this peak (see [17], Section 7.3).

As an example of the application of the *p*-tile and mode methods, consider the cloud-cover picture in Figure 3.1(a); the frequency distribution of its gray levels is given in Table I. If we wish to choose a threshold by the *p*-tile method, say to make the numbers of elements above and below the threshold as nearly equal as possible, it can be verified from Table I that the best place for the threshold is between level 17 and level 18. Similarly, if we wish to choose a threshold by the mode method, it can be seen from the

TABLE I

Gray level	No. of occurrences	Gray level	No. of occurrences
0	406	16	1406
1	249	17	1424
2	293	18	1346
3	439	19	1342
4	784	20	1427
5	1421	21	1395
6	2014	22	1603
7	1651	23	1925
8	1667	24	2116
9	1923	25	3065
10	2105	26	4361
11	1992	27	3673
12	2033	28	2135
13	2248	29	1047
14	2051	30	443
15	1566	31	434

table [or more easily, from the bar graph in Figure 8.2(a)] that the center of the "valley" between the two peaks is between level 18 and level 19. The results of thresholding at the points chosen by the two methods are shown in Figure 8.2(b, c). These results should be compared with Figure 3.1(e), where the threshold was arbitrarily set at the midpoint of the gray scale, i.e., between level 15 and level 16.

Another approach to threshold selection is to test points for membership in the subset sequentially; this makes it possible to vary the threshold in a manner dependent on the nature of the points that have already been accepted. For example, one might accept a new point only if it differs in gray level from the mean of the already accepted points by less than some multiple of their standard deviation (see [19], Section 6.5). A disadvantage of this approach is that the results depend on the sequence in which the points are tested.

REFERENCES

1. A. Rosenfeld, C. Fried, and J. N. Orton, Automatic cloud interpretation, *Photogrammetric Engrg.* **31**, 991–1002 (November 1965).
2. R. Narasimhan and J. P. Fornango, Some further experiments in the parallel processing of pictures, *IEEE Trans. Electronic Computers* **EC-13**, 748–750 (December 1964).

8.2. Subsets Derivable from a Given Subset: 1, Connectivity

Once a subset has been singled out from a picture, it becomes possible to perform operations on the picture in which the points of the subset play special roles. In particular, such operations can be used to derive new subsets from the given one. (If several subsets have been singled out, new ones can be derived from them by set-theoretic operations, such as union, intersection, etc.; but here we shall be primarily concerned with subsets definable in terms of a single given subset.) In this section we consider operations that involve the concept of connectivity.

a. *Border and Interior*

Let S be a subset of a digital picture, and let $\bar{S}$ denote the complement of S (i.e., the set of picture elements not in S). The element (i, j) of S is called *isolated* if all its horizontal and vertical neighbors are in $\bar{S}$; i.e., if all of the elements, $(i - 1, j), (i + 1, j), (i, j - 1)$, and $(i, j + 1)$ are in $\bar{S}$. [Throughout this section, one could define alternative concepts by also using the four "diagonal neighbors" $(i - 1, j - 1), (i - 1, j + 1), (i + 1, j - 1)$, and $(i + 1, j + 1)$.] Similarly, (i, j) is called *interior* if all of these neighbors are in S. If some of the neighbors are in S and some in $\bar{S}$, we call (i, j) a *border* element. In the special case where there are just two *opposite* neighbors [i.e., $(i - 1, j)$ and $(i + 1, j)$, or $(i, j - 1)$ and $(i, j + 1)$] in $\bar{S}$, the other two being in S, we call (i, j) an *arc* element. [If (i, j) has three neighbors in $\bar{S}$, we might call it an *arc end* element.] More refined classes of elements can be defined in terms of having (pairs of) neighbors (or neighbors of neighbors, etc.) in particular directions.

The border (i.e., set of border elements) and interior are trivial examples of new subsets that can be derived from a given one; the following are some less trivial related examples:

1. As indicated in Section 6.4, one can clean up noise in a binary-valued picture by changing 1's to 0's if too many of their neighbors are 0's. In the context of the present section, this can be thought of as singling out the elements of the subset that have many neighbors in the subset as a new subset. For example, if the subset contains solid regions, arcs or curves, and noise points, these different types of parts can be more or less distinguished by suitable thresholding with respect to the number of neighbors in the subset.

2. Suppose that we have thresholded a picture at two levels, $t_1 < t_2$. Let S_2 be the set of elements whose values exceed t_2. We can regard S_2 as the "hard core" of a subset and can attempt to "fill out" this subset by adding in elements whose values exceed t_1, provided that they have a sufficient number of neighbors in S_2.

b. *Connected Components*

We say that the elements (i, j) and (h, k) of S are *connected* if there exists a sequence of elements $(i, j) = (i_0, j_0), (i_1, j_1), \ldots, (i_m, j_m) = (h, k)$, all in S, such that (i_r, j_r) is a neighbor of (i_{r-1}, j_{r-1}), $1 \leq r \leq m$. For any (i, j) in S, the set of (h, k) such that (i, j) and (h, k) are connected is called a (*connected*) *component* of S. A subset S that has only one component is called *connected*.

We can also consider the components of $\bar{S}$. For various reasons [1], it is preferable to use the eight-neighbor definition of "connected" for $\bar{S}$ if we are using the four-neighbor definition for S, and vice versa. We shall assume that any picture is always surrounded by a border of 0's; the component of $\bar{S}$ consisting of the elements connected to (any one of) these 0's is called the *outside* of S. If $\bar{S}$ has any other components, they are called *holes* in S; any element of a hole is said to be *inside* S. If S is connected and has no holes, it is called *simply connected*; if it has holes, it is called *multiply connected*.

c. *Border Following*†

Let S be connected and let B be the set of border elements of S having neighbors in some particular component of $\bar{S}$. Readily, B is connected; moreover, by starting at any element of B and successively moving to neighboring elements in a well-defined way, we can "follow around" B and return to the starting point. The following is an algorithm that follows B counterclockwise, "keeping S on the left"; for the proof that it always works, see [1].

Let $x_0 = (i_0, j_0)$ be the (arbitrary) initial element of B and let $y_1^{(0)}$ be any one of $(i_0 - 1, j_0)$, $(i_0 + 1, j_0)$, $(i_0, j_0 - 1)$, $(i_0, j_0 + 1)$ that is in $\bar{S}$ (at least one of them is in $\bar{S}$ since (i_0, j_0) is a border element of S). Let the *eight* neighbors of (i_0, j_0), in counterclockwise order starting with $y_1^{(0)}$, be $y_1^{(0)}, \ldots, y_8^{(0)}$. If none of $y_3^{(0)}, y_5^{(0)}, y_7^{(0)}$ is in S, then x_0 is the sole element of S, and there is nothing to do. Otherwise, let $y_{2i+1}^{(0)}$ be the first of these y's that is in S; then as the next element x_1 of B, we take

$$y_{2i+1}^{(0)}, \quad \text{if} \quad y_{2i}^{(0)} \text{ is in } \bar{S}$$

$$y_{2i}^{(0)}, \quad \text{if} \quad y_{2i}^{(0)} \text{ is in } S$$

Note that in either case, x_1 is indeed a border element, since its neighbor $y_{2i}^{(0)}$ (or $y_{2i-1}^{(0)}$) is in $\bar{S}$. To find the next element, we take *this neighbor* as $y_1^{(1)}$ and proceed exactly as in the first step; and so on. (The reader is urged to work out a few examples.)

EXERCISE 1. Verify that if eight neighbors are used in the definition of a connected component, the algorithm can be simplified as follows: Let $y_i^{(0)}$ be the first of the $y^{(0)}$'s that is in S; then we can take $x_1 = y_i^{(0)}$ and $y_1^{(1)} = y_{i-1}^{(0)}$.

EXERCISE 2. Let z_0 be any element of B, let z_1 be any of the four neighbors of z_0, and define the succeeding z's as follows: If the last z was in S, turn right; if it was in $\bar{S}$, turn left (see [4], Section 8.4). Show that this procedure will "spiral" counterclockwise around B, provided that B does not "touch itself."

† See [2–8].

There exist techniques for border (i.e., edge) and curve following that can be used with continuous pictures. Imagine that we scan across the picture "helically"; in other words, we move very rapidly around a small circle while the center of the circle moves more slowly across the picture. Suppose that we look for points around the circle at which the derivative of the gray level along the circumference has high absolute value. If the center of the circle is on an edge, there will be two such points approximately 180° apart. As the center moves, these points will come closer together unless the movement has been along the edge. In fact the direction and amount by which the points have shifted can be used to determine how to correct the position of the center to keep it on the edge. This procedure can be modified for following curves rather than edges, using a circle of diameter larger than the thickness of the curves.

d. *Component Labeling*

In the following paragraphs we describe methods of singling out each component of a given picture subset as a separate "object." Let S be the set of 1's in a binary-valued digital picture. We shall distinguish the components of S by "labeling" them; specifically, we shall give each element of S a positive integer value in such a way that all elements in a given component receive the same value, while elements in different components receive different values.

1. "*Propagation.*" Suppose that we examine the elements of the picture systematically in any sequence until an element with value 1 is found; we then give this element a new value, say, 2. We now repeatedly perform a local operation in which any "1" in the picture that has a "2" as a neighbor is itself changed to a "2." If this is done until no further change is possible, we have evidently changed every "1" that belongs to the same component as the original "1" into a "2." Note that the number of repetitions required may be comparable to the number of elements in the picture, e.g., if the component is as shown below:

$$
\begin{array}{l}
11111111111 \\
00000000001 \\
11111111111 \\
10000000000 \\
11111111111
\end{array}
$$

We now resume the systematic scan until another " 1 " is found; evidently this " 1 " must belong to a different component. We give this " 1 " a new value, say, 3 and repeat the above process, changing all the 1's in the new component into 3's. The entire procedure is repeated until the scan has been completed, at which point each component of 1's has been uniquely labeled with an integer ≥ 2. On methods of this type applied to the problem of *counting* connected components (to be discussed further in Section 9.1), see [9–11], as well as [12], Section 5.1.

This method can be modified to require only a single repeated local operation, rather than one such repeated operation for each component found, if we begin by changing each " 1 " in the picture to a different positive integer, e.g., by scanning through the picture and changing the successive 1's to 1, 2, 3, ... We can then repeatedly apply the local operation that changes a_{ij} to, say,

$$\max \{a_{ij}, a_{i-1,j}, a_{i+1,j}, a_{i,j-1}, a_{i,j+1}\}$$

(but not allowing 0's to change). When this has been done until no further change can take place, every element of a given component will have as a label the largest of the values that the elements of that component had initially.

2. *Border following.* Suppose that the picture is scanned row by row from left to right; then the "outside border" of a component of 1's is always first encountered as a transition from 0 to 1, while the border of a hole is first encountered as a transition from 1 to 0. Let us perform such a scan, and whenever we encounter an outside border, follow around it and change the values of its elements from 1 to, say, an integer ≥ 3. Similarly, whenever we encounter the border of a hole, we can follow it and change 1's to 2's but leave integers ≥ 3 unchanged; we will find such integers along the border when the hole and the outside are only one element apart. When a border of either type has been followed completely around, we resume the systematic scan; borders that have already been followed will be ignored when we cross them again, since their elements are not 1's now. When the scan is complete, the outside border of each component of 1's will have a unique label ≥ 3. If desired, we can now "propagate" these labels into the interiors of their components by repeatedly performing a local operation on the picture, as previously

described. (On a border-following scheme for component counting, see pp. 207–211 of [31], Section 7.3.) Alternatively, as soon as an outside border has been completely followed, we can systematically scan its "inside"; each time we find the border of a hole, we can follow it around and then systematically scan *its* "inside"; each time we find an outside border (i.e., a border of a new component that lies inside a hole in the original component), we can follow it around and scan *its* "inside"; and so on (see [12]; compare [8]). This approach has the advantage that it is easy to keep track of which holes are inside each component, which other components are inside each hole, and so on.

3. *"Tracking."* Suppose that we examine the picture row by row; in general each row consists of runs of 0's alternating with runs of 1's. On the first row, we leave the first run of 1's unchanged, change the 1's in the second run to 2's, those in the third run to 3's, and so on. We now examine the runs of 1's on the second row. If such a run does not overlap any run of 1's on the first row, we give the 1's in it a new label; if it overlaps just one such run, we give it the same label as that run; and if it overlaps more than one such run, we give it the smallest of their labels, and record in a "table of equivalences" the fact that these labels all belong to the same connected component. We continue in this way, comparing the runs on each row to the runs on the preceding row, until all rows have been examined. At this point we examine the table of equivalences, and determine, for each label, the smallest label that has been assigned to the same connected component. We then scan through the picture again and replace each label by its smallest equivalent label; this gives each connected component a unique label. On component-counting versions of this technique, see [13], as well as [29], Section 7.3, and [3], Section 8.3.

e. *The Inside and Outside of a Subset*

To determine whether an element of $\bar{S}$ is outside or inside (i.e., in a hole surrounded by) S, we can apply the methods just described to relabel the 0's so that inside and outside 0's have different labels. For example, we can scan around the border of the picture and change all 0's to 2's, and then repeatedly perform a local operation that changes 0's which are neighbors of 2's to 2's. When this has been done until no further change is possible, the outside 0's have all become 2's, while the inside 0's are still 0's.

This relabeling approach may be economical if an inside-outside decision has to be made for many different points; but if it need only be made for a few points, other methods can be used, e.g., algorithms [14–16] for deciding whether a given point is inside or outside a polygon.

f. *Shrinking and Thinning a Subset*

If a subset has many small connected components, one may want to simplify the picture by shrinking each component down to a single element. (This also makes it easy to count the components by counting the resulting elements [17, 18].) Similarly, if a subset is everywhere very elongated (a bubble track, a handwritten word, etc.), one may want to "thin" it into a line drawing.

To replace components by single elements, one can simply label them and then suppress all but one instance of each label; but the labeling step may be very time consuming, particularly if there are many components. The following is a more efficient method of reducing simply connected components of 1's to single 1's. We examine the elements of the picture in succession, and change the value of an element from 1 to 0 if (1) at least one of its neighbors is in S, and at least one of them is in $\bar{S}$; (2) all of its neighbors in S belong to a connected set of 1's in its set of *eight* neighbors. (See [1] for a proof that this algorithm always works. A slightly more complicated algorithm exists that will shrink simply connected components to single elements when it is repeatedly applied to the picture in parallel, i.e., to every element of the picture simultaneously.)

To thin a picture subset, one can remove successive "layers" of border elements from it an appropriate number of times, using the conditions of the shrinking algorithm to prevent the subset from becoming disconnected (see [12], Section 8.4). For some simple thinning algorithms, see [17], Section 5.1; and compare [19, 20]. On the related problem of finding a curve that "fits" a stream of isolated points, see [21].

EXERCISE 3. Verify that if we use the eight-neighbor definition of connectedness, the second condition in the shrinking algorithm can be simplified to: "(2) Its set of neighbors in S is connected."

EXERCISE 4. Call an element of S an "end" if it has three neighbors in $\bar{S}$; a "corner" if it has just two consecutive neighbors in S and the diagonal neighbor between them is also in S. Let ϕ be the operation that deletes ends,

139

"northwest" corners, and "northeast" corners, *except* for the boldfaced elements in the following two cases (where the *'s can be either 0 or 1):

$$
\begin{array}{ccc}
* & 0 & * \\
0 & 1 & 0 \\
0 & 1 & 0 \\
* & 0 & *
\end{array}
\qquad \text{and} \qquad
\begin{array}{cccc}
* & 0 & 0 & * \\
0 & \mathbf{1} & 1 & 0 \\
* & 0 & 0 & *
\end{array}
$$

Verify that if ϕ is applied repeatedly to every element of the picture in parallel, it shrinks every simply connected component of 1's down to a single element.

REFERENCES

1. A. Rosenfeld, Connectivity in digital pictures, *J. ACM.* **16**, in press (1969).
2. E. C. Greanias, P. F. Meagher, R. J. Norman, and P. Essinger, The recognition of handwritten numerals by contour analysis, *IBM J. Res. Develop.* **7**, 14–21 (January 1963).
3. J. A. Bradshaw, Letter recognition using a captive scan, *IEEE Trans. Electronic Computers* **EC-12**, 26 (February 1963).
4. N. Sezaki and H. Katagiri, Character recognition by follow method, *Proc. IEEE* **53**, 510 (May 1965).
5. N. Sezaki, H. Katagiri, and T. Kaneko, Pattern reproduction by follow method, *ibid.* **53**, 1656–1657 (October 1965).
6. R. S. Ledley, J. D. Jacobsen, and M. Belson, BUGSYS: a programming system for picture processing—not for debugging, *Comm. ACM* **9**, 79–84 (February 1966).
7. R. S. Ledley, L. S. Rotolo, M. Belson, J. Jacobsen, J. B. Wilson, and T. Golab, Pattern recognition studies in the biomedical sciences, *SJCC* pp. 411–430 (May 1966).
8. W. M. Rintala and C. C. Hsu, A feature-detection program for patterns with overlapping cells, *IEEE Trans. Systems Science and Cybernetics* **SSC-4**, 16–23 (March 1968).
9. R. A. Kirsch, L. Cahn, C. Ray, and G. H. Urban, Experiments in processing pictorial information with a digital computer, *EJCC* pp. 221–229 (December 1957).
10. P. Weston, Photocell field counts random objects, *Electronics* **34**, 46–47 (September 22, 1961).
11. M. L. Babcock, Some physiology of automata, *WJCC* pp. 291–298 (May 1961).
12. R. S. Ledley, L. S. Rotolo, T. J. Golab, J. D. Jacobsen, M. D. Ginsberg, and J. B. Wilson, FIDAC: Film input to digital automatic computer and associated syntax-directed pattern-recognition programming system, OEOIP, pp. 591–613.
13. T. C. Nuttall, Apparatus for counting objects, U.S. Patent 2803406 (August 20, 1957).
14. M. Shimrat, Position of point relative to polygon, Algorithm 112, *Comm. ACM* **5**,

434 (August 1962); see also R. Hacker, Certification of Algorithm 112, Position of point relative to polygon, *ibid.* **5**, 606 (December 1962).

15. R. G. Loomis, Boundary networks, *ibid.* **8**, 44–48 (January 1965).
16. S. Nordbeck and B. Rystedt, Computer cartography—point-in-polygon programs, *Nordisk Tidskr. Informations-Behandling (BIT)* 7, 30–64 (1967).
17. K. Preston, Jr., The CELLSCAN system, a leucocyte pattern analyzer, *WJCC* pp. 173–183 (May 1961).
18. N. F. Izzo and W. Coles, Blood cell scanner identifies rare cells, *Electronics* **35**, 52–57 (April 27, 1962).
19. P. Saraga and D. J. Woollons, The design of operations for pattern processing, *CPR*, pp. 106–116.
20. C. J. Hilditch, Linear skeletons from square cupboards,‘ Machine Intelligence 4 ” (B. Meltzer and D. Michie, eds.), pp. 403–420. American Elsevier, New York, 1969.
21. P. H. A. Sneath, A method for curve seeking from scattered points, *Comput. J.* **8**, 383–391 (January 1966).

8.3. Subsets Derivable from a Given Subset: 2, Distance

Let A be the set of all pairs of integers and let d be a function that takes pairs of elements of A into nonnegative integers. We call d a *distance function* if it is *positive definite, symmetric*, and satisfies the *triangle inequality*—in other words, if for all x, y, z in A, we have

$$d(x, y) = 0 \quad \text{if and only if} \quad x = y$$
$$d(x, y) = d(y, x)$$
$$d(x, z) \leq d(x, y) + d(y, z)$$

If B is any subset of A, by $d(x, B)$ we mean $\min_{y \text{ in } B} d(x, y)$, i.e., the least of the distances from x to the elements of B.

The following are two useful examples of distance functions:

1. $$d_1((i, j), (h, k)) = |i - h| + |j - k|$$

For this function ("city-block distance"), the set of (h, k) at distance $\leq r$ from (i, j) has the shape of a *diamond* (i.e., a square with sides inclined at $\pm 45°$) of side length $r\sqrt{2}$ and with center at (i, j). In particular, the (h, k)'s at distance 1 from (i, j) are just the four horizontal and vertical neighbors of (i, j).

2. $$d_2((i, j), (h, k)) = \max(|i - h|, |j - k|)$$

Here the set of (h, k) at distance $\leq r$ from (i, j) is a *square* (with sides horizon-

141

tal and vertical) of side length $2r$ and with center at (i, j), and the (h, k)'s at distance 1 from (i, j) are the eight neighbors of (i, j).

It is also possible to define distance functions for which the set of elements at a given distance from a given point is an *octagon* or (approximately) a *hexagon*. (One can get "true" hexagons by converting the "square" array A into a "hexagonal" array, e.g., by shifting alternate rows distance $\frac{1}{2}$ to the right.)

EXERCISE 1. Show that if we define $d((i, j), (h, k))$ to be the integer closest to $[(i - h)^2 + (j - k)^2]^{1/2}$, it is *not* a distance function.

We call a distance function *regular* if it has the following property: For all x, z in A, there exists y in A such that $d(x, y) = 1$ and $d(y, z) = d(x, z) - 1$. Readily, d_1 and d_2 are regular. It is not difficult to establish, using induction, the following algorithm for computing a regular distance function from the set of 0's (which we assume to be nonempty) in a binary-valued digital picture.

THEOREM. Let d be a regular distance function; let (a_{ij}) be an n-by-n binary-valued digital picture; let S be the set of (i, j) for which $a_{ij} = 0$; and let the sequence of integer-valued pictures $(a_{ij}^{(k)})$ be defined by

$$a_{ij}^{(k)} = \min_{d((u, v), (i, j)) \leq 1} a_{uv}^{(k-1)} + a_{ij}^{(0)}$$

for $k = 1, 2, \ldots$, where $a_{ij}^{(0)} = a_{ij}$. Then, for sufficiently high k (e.g., for d_1, we can take $k = 2n$; for d_2, $k = n$ suffices), we have $a_{ij}^{(k)} = d((i, j), S)$ for all (i, j).

In fact it is easily seen that this algorithm successively changes all interior 1's to 2's, all interior 2's to 3's, ..., until no further change is possible (compare [9] in Section 8.2). It can be verified that if we generate the sequence $a_{ij}^{(k)}$ using the d_1 and d_2 algorithms at alternate steps, we obtain an "octagon" distance. "Diamond," "square," and "octagon" distances from a single "0" are shown in Figure 8.3. Note that the algorithm can also be applied to nonbinary pictures [6]; if we assume that the original gray levels $a_{ij}^{(0)}$ are all between 0 and 1, then the resulting "distance" goes up rapidly (i.e., about as fast as the actual distance does) in regions where the gray levels are close to 1, and slowly where they are close to 0.

Distance functions can be used to derive various types of picture subsets from a given subset. In the following examples, S^r denotes the set of (i, j)

```
                            3
                          3 2 3
                        3 2 1 2 3
        (a)   3 2 1 0 1 2 3
                        3 2 1 2 3
                          3 2 3
                            3
```

```
              3 3 3 3 3 3 3
              3 2 2 2 2 2 3
              3 2 1 1 1 2 3
        (b)   3 2 1 0 1 2 3
              3 2 1 1 1 2 3
              3 2 2 2 2 2 3
              3 3 3 3 3 3 3
```

```
                3 3 3
              3 2 2 2 3
            3 2 2 1 2 2 3
        (c) 3 2 1 0 1 2 3
            3 2 2 1 2 2 3
              3 2 2 2 3
                3 3 3
```

Figure 8.3. Distances from a single "0": (a) d_1, diamonds, (b) d_2, squares, (c) d_1 alternating with d_2, octagons.

such that $d((i, j), S) \leq r$. By the *d-disk of radius r* centered at (i, j), we mean the set of (h, k) such that $d((i, j), (h, k)) \leq r$.

a. *Isolated Parts of a Subset*

Let C be any connected component of S^r. If C has area close to that of the *d*-disk of radius r, the part of S that it contains must be small in size compared to r, and since this part of S is at least $2r$ away from every other element of S, it can legitimately be called "isolated."

b. *Clusters and Elongated Parts of a Subset*†

For sufficiently large r, S^r contains the entire picture, so that its complement $\overline{S^r}$ is empty; whence so is $(\overline{S^r})^s$ for any s. On the other hand, for $r = 0$,

† Compare [20], Section 5.1.

143

S^r is the same as S, so that $\overline{(S^0)^s} = \overline{S}^s$ contains $\overline{S}$ for all s. Thus, for any (i, j) not in S, there exists a smallest r (call it r_{ij}), evidently >0, such that (i, j) is not contained in $\overline{(S^r)^r}$. We call this r_{ij} the *radius of fusion* of s at (i, j); if (i, j) is in S, we define $r_{ij} = 0$. Intuitively, $r_{ij} \leq r$ means that if S is "expanded" by r increments (i.e., each point of S is replaced by a d-disk of radius r), and then "recontracted" by the same amount, (i, j) is in the resulting set. If (i, j) is not in the original S, this can only happen because several expanded pieces of S have "fused" together, so that there is no place near enough to (i, j) for the recontraction to start from, and (i, j) remains even after the recontraction. For an illustration of this concept, see Figure 8.4.

Figure 8.4. Illustration of "fusion" using "octagon" distance and a set S consisting of three elements (denoted by 0's). (a) S^1, the set of elements at distance ≤ 1 from S. Note that each of the 1's is a border element of S^1. In other words, each of them is at distance 1 from the complement $\overline{S^1}$, i.e., each is in $(\overline{S^1})^1$, so that if S^1 is "recontracted" by one increment, only the 0's remain; nothing has "fused." (b) S^2, the set of elements at "octagon" distances ≤ 2 from S. (c) S^2 with the elements of $(\overline{S^2})^1$ deleted. (d) S^2 with the elements of $(\overline{S^2})^2$ deleted. The non-0's that remain are elements of $\overline{S}$ at which the radius of fusion is 2.

(a)
```
        1                    2 1 2
      1 0 1                  1 0 1
        1                    2 1 2 2
        1       1            2 1 2 2 1 2
      1 0 1 1 0 1            1 0 1 1 0 1
        1                    2 1 2 2 1 2
```
(c)

(b)
```
      2 2 2
    2 2 1 2 2
    2 1 0 1 2                        0
    2 2 1 2 2 2 2                    1
    2 2 1 2 2 1 2 2       (d)        1 2
    2 1 0 1 1 0 1 2                  0 1 1 0
    2 2 1 2 2 1 2 2
      2 2 2 2 2 2
```

EXERCISE 2. What are the radii of fusion for the set of points (ki, kj), where i, j, k are integers, using the distances d_1 and d_2 ?

Let S_t be the set of points at which $r_{ij} \leq t$, and let C be a connected component of S_t. Readily, if the area of C is large compared to t^2, then C must have arisen from the "fusion" of a *cluster* of elements of S; the larger we must take t in order for this to happen, the sparser the cluster must have been.

```
0 0
0 1 0
0 1 1 0
0 1 2 1 0
0 1 2 2 1 0
0 1 2 3 2 1 0
0 1 2 3 3 2 1 0
0 1 2 3 4 3 2 1 0
0 1 2 3 3 3 3 2 1 0
0 1 2 2 2 2 2 2 1 0
0 1 1 1 1 1 1 1 1 1 0
0 0 0 0 0 0 0 0 0 0 0
```

(a)

Figure 8.5. Distances—(a) "diamond," (b) "square," (c) "octagon"—from the elements of a triangle to the 0's surrounding it; skeleton elements are in boldface type. In (a), an element is in the skeleton if none of its four neighbors has a value larger than its own; in (b) if none of its eight neighbors has such a value; while in (c) the four-neighbor criterion is used if the value of the element is odd, the eight-neighbor criterion if its value is even. It may be verified that in each case the triangle is the union of the "disks"—diamonds, squares, or octagons, respectively—centered at the skeleton elements, where the radius of each disk is one less than the the value of the skeleton element at its center.

```
0 0
0 1 0
0 1 1 0
0 1 1 1 0
0 1 2 1 1 0
0 1 2 2 1 1 0
0 1 2 2 2 1 1 0
0 1 2 3 2 2 1 1 0
0 1 2 3 3 2 2 1 1 0
0 1 2 2 2 2 2 2 1 1 0
0 1 1 1 1 1 1 1 1 1 1 0
0 0 0 0 0 0 0 0 0 0 0 0
```

(b)

```
0 0
0 1 0
0 1 1 0
0 1 2 1 0
0 1 2 2 1 0
0 1 2 2 2 1 0
0 1 2 3 2 2 1 0
0 1 2 3 3 2 2 1 0
0 1 2 3 3 3 2 2 1 0
0 1 2 2 2 2 2 2 2 1 0
0 1 1 1 1 1 1 1 1 1 1 0
0 0 0 0 0 0 0 0 0 0 0 0
```

(c)

Similarly, let r'_{ij} be the radius of fusion of $\bar{S}$ at (i,j); let S_t' be the set of points at which $r'_{ij} \leq t$, and let $S_t^* = S - S_t'$. Readily, if a connected component of S_t^* has an area large compared to t^2, it must be an *elongated part* of S, since in spite of its large area, it "disappears" under expansion and recontraction of $\bar{S}$ by r increments, and so cannot be more than $2r$ wide at any point.

c. The "Skeleton" of a Subset

The set of elements from which the distance to $\bar{S}$ is a (not necessarily strict) local maximum constitutes a sort of "skeleton" of S. (It can be shown [3] that these elements and the associated values of the distance completely determine S.) The set of elements at which there are sharp angles in the "contours of constant distance" (i.e., the loci of elements at a fixed distance from $\bar{S}$) and the set of elements for which there are two or more nearest elements of $\bar{S}$ are also skeleton-like. Skeletons provide an alternative approach to thinning S; they can also be used to abstract information about its shape (e.g., "lobes" on S correspond to "branches" on its skeleton). The distance-maxima skeletons of a triangle, for "diamond," "square," and "octagon" distances, are shown in Figure 8.5; the "octagon" distance-maximum skeleton of the "clouds" in Figure 3.1(e) is shown in Figure 8.6.

EXERCISE 3. Let

$$c_{ij}^{(k)} = c_{i-1,j}^{(k-1)} + c_{i+1,j}^{(k-1)} + c_{i,j-1}^{(k-1)} + c_{i,j+1}^{(k-1)}, \qquad k = 1, 2, \ldots$$

where $c_{ij}^{(0)} = c_{ij}$. Prove that $c_{ij}^{(k)}$ is the sum of the gray levels at the ends of all city-block paths of length k from (i,j). [*Hint:* A path of length k from (i,j) consists of the step from (i,j) to one of its neighbors, followed by a path of length $k-1$ from that neighbor.] Note that if (c_{ij}) is binary-valued, then $c_{ij}^{(k)}$ is the same as the number of paths of length k from (i,j) to the set of 1's in (c_{ij}).

★ EXERCISE 4. Let

$$h_{ij}^{(k)} = h_{i,j-1}^{(k-1)} + h_{i,j+1}^{(k-1)} - h_{ij}^{(k-2)}, \qquad k = 3, 4, \ldots$$

where $h_{ij}^{(0)} = c_{ij}$, $h_{ij}^{(1)} = c_{i,j-1} + c_{i,j+1}$, and $h_{ij}^{(2)} = h_{i,j-1}^{(1)} + h_{i,j+1}^{(1)} - 2h_{ij}^{(0)}$.

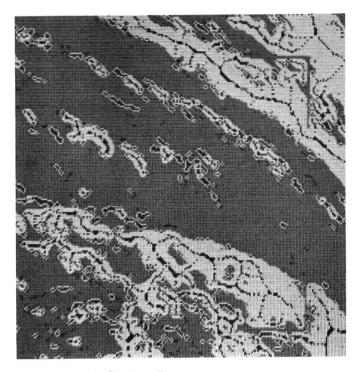

Figure 8.6. Distance-maxima skeleton ("octagon"
distances from the noncloud) for Figure 3.1(e). For
clarity, the noncloud is shown as medium gray, while the
skeleton elements all have gray levels darker than
medium, but proportional to their associated distance
values.

Let
$$d_{ij}^{(k)} = d_{i-1,j}^{(k-1)} + d_{i+1,j}^{(k-1)} - d_{ij}^{(k-2)} + h_{ij}^{(k)} - h_{ij}^{(k-2)}, \qquad k = 2, 3, \dots$$

where $d_{ij}^{(0)} = c_{ij}$ and $d_{ij}^{(1)} = c_{i, j-1} + c_{i, j+1} + c_{i-1, j} + c_{i+1, j}$. Prove that
$d_{ij}^{(k)}$ is the sum of the gray levels of the elements at city-block distance k from
(i, j). Note that if (c_{ij}) is binary-valued, then $d_{ij}^{(k)}$ is the same as the number of
1's at distance k from (i, j).

EXERCISE 5. Devise algorithms for counting (a) the number of *shortest* paths
from (i, j) to the set S of all 1's, and (b) the number of 1's at distance $d((i, j), S)$
from (i, j).

147

REFERENCES

1. H. Blum, An associative machine for dealing with the visual field and some of its biological implications, BPSS, pp. 244–260.
2. H. Blum, A transformation for extracting new descriptors of shape, MPSVF, pp. 362-380.
3. A. Rosenfeld and J. L. Pfaltz, Sequential operations in digital picture processing, *J. ACM* **13**, 471–494 (October 1966).
4. J. L. Pfaltz and A. Rosenfeld, Computer representation of planar regions by their skeletons, *Comm. ACM* **10**, 119–125 (February 1967).
5. L. Calabi and W. E. Hartnett, Shape recognition, prairie fires, convex deficiencies and skeletons, *Amer. Math. Monthly* **75**, 335–342 (April 1968).
6. D. Rutovitz, Data structures for operations on digital images, PPR, pp. 105–133.
7. O. Philbrick, Shape description with the medial axis transformation, *ibid.*, pp. 395–407.
8. A. Rosenfeld and J. L. Pfaltz, Distance functions on digitial pictures, *Pattern Recognition* **1**, 33–61 (July 1968).
9. T. Kasvand, Histogramming of nerve fiber cross-sections and water droplets by methods of pattern recognition, CPR, pp. 315–326.
10. U. Montanari, A method of obtaining skeletons using a quasi-Euclidean distance, *J. ACM* **15**, 600–624 (October 1968).

8.4. Subsets Derivable from a Given Subset: 3, Direction and Shape

a. *Directed Parts and Shadows of a Subset*

Just as one can define subsets of a continuous or digital picture in terms of the distances of points from a given subset, so one can define subsets in terms of the direction to a given subset. For example, one can distinguish those points of a subset that have other points of the subset as neighbors in given directions; for a line-drawing type of picture, this method can be used to label each point of a curve with the approximate direction of the curve at the point. As another example, one can take as a new subset the set of points that are hidden by a given subset when one looks toward it from far away in a given direction; these are just the points that would be in shadow if the given subset were illuminated by a parallel beam of light from the given direction [1]. More generally, one can take as a new subset the set of points through which a ray in a given direction intersects the given subset a given number of times [2, 3]; compare also [5] in Section 9.4. The areas of such sets can be taken as properties of the given subset (Chapter 9).

EXERCISE 1. Verify that the areas A_L and A_B that are in shadow when the subset is illuminated from the left and from below, respectively, can be used as properties to distinguish the sets of 1's in the six pictures in Exercise 1, Section 6.1.

b. *Convexity*

The picture subset S is called *convex* if, for any two points in S, each point of the line segment joining them is also in S. [Thus convexity is a linear threshold property with respect to a set of properties of order 3 (see Section 8.3).] If A is any subset of a picture, the smallest convex subset containing A is called the *convex hull* of A. On representations of a polygon as a union of convex polygons, see [11], Section 9.4.

EXERCISE 2. (a) Verify that an ellipse is convex. (b) Verify that an arc is convex if and only if it is a straight-line segment.

c. *Edge and Curve Segmentation*

There are several possible methods of selecting "break points" at which the edge or border of a picture subset can be segmented. If the subset is a curve, these methods can be used to segment the subset itself, not merely its edge.

1. *Position extrema.* One can take (locally) highest, lowest, rightmost, or leftmost points of the edge as break points [4].

2. *Points of inflection.* An edge can be divided into successive convex and concave pieces ("peninsulas" and "bays") by breaking it at points where its tangent crosses it [5].

3. *Curvature maxima.* Intuitively, the best points at which to segment an edge in order to approximate it by a polygon are the points at which its direction changes abruptly ("angles"), or where its curvature is high—in particular, where its curvature is a local maximum ([2], Section 3.4). Alternatively, one can segment an edge at points where its curvature changes significantly (e.g., [6]).

EXERCISE 3. What are the position extrema, points of inflection, and curvature maxima for the ellipse $x^2/a^2 + y^2/b^2 = 1$?

4. *Shape features.* One can define criteria for detecting (straight) "strokes," "bays," "notches," "spurs," etc., in an edge. The existence or number

of such pieces can also be used as a property of the given picture subset (Chapter 9). See, e.g., [10], Section 5.1; [2], Section 8.2; as well as [7–10].

5. *Shape matching*. More generally, one can look for pieces of an edge that match given arcs, or that match given pieces of other edges [11]. It is not necessary to perform two-dimensional matching (as in Section 6.1) to do this; instead, one can describe the pieces by functions of a single variable (e.g., by their intrinsic equations; see Section 9.4), and then match these functions. The function matching can be done sequentially, comparing the values of the given and unknown functions point by point. Here minor deviations can be overlooked if one looks ahead and finds that the match resumes. The sequential approach makes it possible to use adjustable match criteria that depend on the past history of the piece being matched.

6. *Nodes*. A curve can be subdivided at " nodes " where arcs end or intersect. This breaks it into " branches " joining the nodes to one another ([12]; see also [13]).

EXERCISE 4. Give descriptions of the capital letters in the typeface used in this book in terms of nodes joined by branches. Specifically, for each letter, assign labels to its nodes and list the pairs of labels corresponding to nodes that are joined by branches. Refine these descriptions by breaking the branches up into shape features in such a way that each letter has a unique description.

d. *Tracking*

Another way of singling out various types of pieces of a picture subset is to " track " the subset from row to row of the picture. Here a natural choice is to take as break points the rows in which runs of points of the subset begin or end, merge or split, or change radically in length or position [14–19]. (The succession of run lengths and positions can also be used to provide simplified descriptions of the shapes of the pieces, e.g., constant width, converging, diverging; horizontal, vertical, diagonal; etc.)

More generally, one can look for successive runs (or run ends) that lie on or near a curve having any prespecified shape; e.g., one can " track " runs that lie along a straight line, a circular arc, etc. This latter type of tracking is used extensively in nuclear bubble chamber picture processing (see [11–14] in Section 7.1). As in the case of shape matching by edge following, deviations or gaps in the piece being followed can be tolerated if they are not too large. Here too, one can vary the tracking criteria in a manner dependent on the history of the piece being tracked.

150

The pieces obtained by tracking from row to row will depend somewhat on the orientation of the given subset with respect to the rows. One way to minimize this is to normalize the subset in orientation. For example, as in picture normalization (Section 7.2), one can put the principal axis of the subset (i.e., of the binary-valued picture that is its characteristic function) in a standard orientation, e.g., perpendicular to the rows. Alternatively, one can find the smallest circumscribed rectangle of the subset, and orient it so that its long side is perpendicular to the rows [20, 21].

EXERCISE 5. Define "pieces" for the capital letters of Exercise 4, using horizontal rows.

e. *Coordinate Conversion*

The presence of an arc of specified shape in a line-drawing picture can often be detected by performing an appropriate coordinate transformation. For example, suppose that we wish to determine whether the picture contains a straight line (of 1's) of a given slope m. To do this, we can transform to new coordinates defined by

$$x' = x, \qquad y' = y - mx$$

In the new coordinate system, the line $y = mx + b$ has become $y' = b$. If we now "collapse" the transformed picture onto the y'-axis (i.e., sum or integrate it in the x direction), we obtain a function of y' that will tend to have a sharp, high peak at $y' = b$ for each y-intercept b of a line of slope m in the original picture. The higher the proportion of 1's in these lines to 1's in other parts of the original picture, the easier these peaks will be to detect. Note that the lines need not be continuous; dotted lines can also be detected by this method if they contain a large enough fraction of the 1's in the picture. Related schemes can be devised to detect other simple shapes, such as circular arcs [22].

An interesting alternative scheme for detecting straight lines [23] makes use of a "point-line transformation" ϕ defined as follows: For every point (x_i, y_i) in the given subset (i.e., for every "1" in the given picture f), we put 1's in the transformed picture $\phi(f)$ at all points of the line $y = y_i x + x_i$. It is easily verified that if the points $(x_1, y_1), \ldots, (x_n, y_n)$ are collinear, the corresponding lines are concurrent, i.e., all pass through a single point. [If the points are on a line that is nearly parallel to the x axis, the lines become nearly parallel, so that their common point recedes to infinity. This difficulty can be avoided by also using another point-line transformation that takes (x_i, y_i) into $y = x_i x + y_i$.] Thus, if we scan f, and each time a " 1 " is found, store 1's at the points of the corresponding line in $\phi(f)$ (we can think of $\phi(f)$ as an array of counters), the presence of many collinear 1's in f will give rise to a point in $\phi(f)$ with a high value. Consequently, the lines of 1's in f can be detected by thresholding $\phi(f)$. If f contains many 1's, it may be desirable to "sample" it, e.g., by scanning across it along several lines at various orientations. If there is a line of 1's in f, at least some of these scans will hit it, so that it can be detected without having to transform every " 1 " in f into a line in $\phi(f)$.

REFERENCES

1. H. A. Glucksman, A parapropagation pattern classifier, *IEEE Trans. Electronic Computers* **EC-14**, 434–443 (June 1965).
2. H. A. Glucksman, Classification of mixed-font alphabets by characteristic loci, *Proc. IEEE Comput. Confer.* pp. 138–141 (September 1967).
3. M. E. Stevens, Abstract shape recognition by machine, *EJCC* pp. 332–351 (December 1961).
4. S. J. Mason and J. K. Clemens, Character recognition in an experimental reading machine, "Recognizing Patterns: Studies in Living and Automatic Systems" (P. A. Kolers and M. Eden, eds.), pp. 156–167. M.I.T. Press, Cambridge, Massachusetts, 1968.
5. H. Freeman, On the classification of line-drawing data, MPSVF, pp. 408–412.
6. M. Symons, A new self-organizing pattern recognition system, CPR, pp. 11–20.
7. R. J. Spinrad, Machine recognition of hand printing, *Information and Control* **8**, 124–142 (April 1965).
8. J. H. Munson, The recognition of hand-printed text, PR^2, pp. 115–140.
9. E. S. Deutsch, Preprocessing for character recognition, CPR, pp. 179–190.
10. H. Genchi, K.-I. Mori, S. Watanabe, and S. Katsuragi, Recognition of handwritten numerical characters for automatic letter sorting, *Proc. IEEE* **56**, 1292–1301 (August 1968.)
11. H. Freeman and L. Garder, Apictorial jigsaw puzzles: the computer solution of a problem in pattern recognition, *IEEE Trans. Electronic Computers* **EC-13**, 118–127 (April 1964).
12. H. Sherman, A quasi-topological method for the recognition of line patterns, *Proc. Intern. Confer. Inform. Process., UNESCO, Paris, 1959* pp. 232–238. UNESCO, Paris, 1960.

13. M. J. Minneman, Handwritten character recognition employing topology, cross correlation, and decision theory, *IEEE Trans. Systems Science and Cybernetics* **SSC-2**, 86–96 (December 1966).

14. R. L. Grimsdale, F. H. Sumner, C. J. Tunis, and T. Kilburn, "A system for the automatic recognition of patterns, *Proc. IEE* **106B**, 210–221 (1959); reprinted in PR, pp. 317–338.

15. R. L. Grimsdale and J. M. Bullingham, Character recognition by digital computer using a special flying-spot scanner, *Comput. J.* **4**, 129–136 (July 1961).

16. I. H. Sublette and J. Tults, Character recognition by digital feature detection, *RCA Rev.* **23**, 60–79 (March 1962).

17. G. U. Uyehara, A stream-following technique for use in character recognition, *IEEE Intern. Conv. Record* Part 4, pp. 64–74 (March 1963).

18. P. G. Perotto, A new method for automatic character recognition, *IEEE Trans. Electronic Computers* **EC-12**, 521–526 (October 1963).

19. K. H. Hocking and J. Thompson, A feature detection method for optical character recognition, CPR, pp. 271–281.

20. P. W. Neurath, B. L. Bablouzian, T. H. Warms, R. C. Serbagi, and A. Falek, "Human chromosome analysis by computer—an optical pattern recognition problem, *Ann. New York Acad. Sci.* **128**, 1013–1028 (January 1966).

21. D. Rutovitz, Machines to classify chromosomes?, "Human Radiation Cytogenetics" (H. J. Evans, W. M. Court Brown, and A.S. McLean, eds.), pp. 58–89. North-Holland, Amsterdam, 1967.

22. M. J. Bazin and J. W. Benoit, Off-line global approach to pattern recognition for bubble chamber pictures, *IEEE Trans. Nuclear Science* **NS-12**, 291–295 (August 1965).

23. P. V. C. Hough, Method and means for recognizing complex patterns, U.S. Patent 3069654 (December 18, 1962).

153

CHAPTER 9

Geometrical Properties of Picture Subsets

As pointed out at the beginning of Chapter 7, certain picture properties have natural definitions only if a distinguished subset of the picture, an "object," is explicitly singled out from the picture. Given a subset, one can compute various picture properties over the subset only (e.g., first change all gray levels outside the subset to zero); these properties can be regarded as properties of the subset. Another important class of subset properties, which we shall survey in this chapter, relates to the *geometry* of the subset, i.e., connectivity, size, shape, etc., and does not depend on the gray levels in it. By a "property," we shall here again usually mean a real number, but we shall also briefly consider "properties" that are functions of a single variable.

9.1. Topological Properties

Geometrical properties that remain invariant under arbitrary "rubber-sheet" distortions of the picture are called *topological* properties. Note that by this definition, the property of being line–drawing-like is not topological, since on a real picture, lines have finite widths and can be stretched into wide subsets. However, if we regard line drawings as idealized, with their lines replaced by mathematical lines, or if we allow only distortions that preserve line-likeness, then various properties of a line drawing, such as the orders of (i.e., numbers of arcs meeting at) its "nodes" (Section 8.4), become topological properties.

a. *Connectivity and Order of Connectivity*

The most familiar topological property of a picture subset is its *connectivity*, i.e., the number of its connected components. Evidently, any of the component labeling methods described in Section 8.2 can be used to count

155

the components. For example, in the "propagation" technique, the number of times a "1" is found by the systematic scan is the same as the number of components; in the "border following" technique, similarly, we need only count the number of times that an outside border is found. Special techniques, to be described below, can be used to count simply connected objects.

Let S be a connected picture subset; then the number of components of its complement $\bar{S}$ is called the *order of connectivity* of S. (Note that this number is just one greater than the number of "holes" in S; in particular, S is simply connected if and only if its order of connectivity is 1.)

b. *The Genus*

The number of components of the subset S, minus the number of holes in S, is called the *genus* (or *Euler number*) of S; we shall denote this number by G_S.

EXERCISE 1. Tabulate the connectivity, order of connectivity, and genus for each lowercase vowel in the typeface used in this book.

THEOREM. For any subset S of a digital picture, we have

$$G_S = I_S - II_S + IV_S$$

where I_S is the number of elements in S, II_S is the number of horizontally or vertically adjacent pairs of elements in S, and IV_S is the number of two-by-two squares of horizontally and vertically adjacent elements in S.

EXERCISE 2. Prove the theorem by induction on I_S.

This theorem is, in fact, the "dual" of a more familiar one on polygonal networks (or on polyhedra): $G = V - E + F$, where V, E, F are the numbers of vertices, edges, and faces, respectively.

Note that by this theorem, the property of having a given genus is a linear threshold property with respect to a set of local properties of orders ≤ 4 (Section 8.3). It can be shown, in fact, that functions of G_S are the only topological properties of bounded order. (We recall that connectivity itself has order that grows with the size of the picture.)

The theorem provides us with a simple method of computing G_S. In fact let S be the set of 1's in the binary-valued digital picture (a_{ij}), and let

$$b_{ij} = a_{ij}(a_{i-1,j} + a_{i+1,j} + a_{i,i-1} + a_{i,j+1})/2$$

$$c_{ij} = a_{ij}(a_{i-1,j-1}a_{i-1,j}a_{i,i-1} + a_{i-1,j}a_{i-1,j+1}a_{i,j+1}$$

$$+ a_{i,j-1}a_{i+1,j-1}a_{i+1,j} + a_{i,j+1}a_{i+1,j}a_{i+1,j+1})/4$$

Then readily $\sum a_{ij} = I_S$, $\sum b_{ij} = II_S$, $\sum c_{ij} = IV_S$, where the sums are taken over all (i,j) in the picture.

If we know that every connected component of S is simply connected, then G_S reduces to the connectivity of S, so that we can count the number of components of S by computing G_S. (On this approach, see [11] in Section 8.2.) We now describe two other methods of component counting in the simply connected case, based on techniques described in Section 8.2.

1. *Tracking.* On the first row of the picture, we count the runs of 1's. On the second and succeeding rows, we add one to the count for each run that does not overlap a run on the preceding row; do nothing for runs that overlap just one run on the preceding row; and subtract k from the count for each run that overlaps $k + 1$ runs on the preceding row ($k = 1, 2, \ldots$). When all rows have been examined, the final count is the same as the number of components. Note that if a component has a hole, a run will split into two or more and later remerge; and we will incorrectly subtract one or more from the count when it remerges, since we have no way of knowing that the parts had originally been counted as only a single component. In fact, if this counting method is applied to a picture in which the components of 1's are not necessarily simply connected, it will compute the genus.

It is of interest to note that if we want not only to count components by this method, but also to compute their areas, we can do both correctly even though the components are not simply connected. Specifically, we can proceed as follows: We assign a counter to each run of 1's on the first row, and store in it the length of that run. On the second and succeeding rows, we start a new counter for each run that does not overlap a run on the preceding row; if a run overlaps just one run on the preceding row, we add its length to the contents of the corresponding counter; and if a run overlaps two or more runs on the preceding row, we merge the contents of their counters and add the new run length to the sum. When all rows have been examined, the number of counters containing nonzero values is the number of components, and the value in each counter is the area of the corresponding component.

157

2. *Shrinking.* The shrinking algorithm described in Section 8.2 reduces simply connected components to single elements, but a component containing a hole can only shrink to a closed curve, Thus, if after the shrinking has been completed, we find that no two 1's in the final picture are adjacent, the components of the original figure must have all been simply connected, and the number of 1's in the final picture is then equal to the number of these components.

9.2. Metric Properties: Size

In this and the next section we discuss picture subset properties that involve the measurements of areas, distances, angles, etc.; such properties are called *metric properties.*

a. *Area and Perimeter*

The area of a subset of a digital picture is just the number of elements in the subset; it can be obtained by counting the 1's (or equivalently, adding up all the elements) in the characteristic function of the subset. As mentioned above, the areas of the connected components of a subset can be obtained by a modification of the "tracking" method of component counting. The areas of various subsets derived from a given subset (e.g., the sets of points at given distances from it, its convex hull, its "shadows," etc.) can also be used as properties of the original subset.

To obtain the perimeter of a subset, one can follow its edges and measure the total distance traversed. For digital pictures, one can take the perimeter of a subset as being approximately proportional to the area of its border (or, somewhat more accurately, to the average of the area of its border and the area of its complement's border). The arc length of a line-like subset can be measured similarly. On algorithms for measuring area, perimeter, etc. for chain-encoded line drawings, see [1].

For continuous pictures, perimeter and arc length cannot, in general, be measured exactly; however, one can approximate an arc by an inscribed polygon. Evidently, the arc length obtained in this way increases (or at least does not decrease) as the lengths of the sides of this polygon decrease. One can thus speak of the "ε-length" of an arc [2], where ε is the smallest length of side of inscribed polygon that is used to approximate the arc length. Note that this is approximately equal to $1/2\varepsilon$ times the area of the set of points at distances $\leq \varepsilon$ from the arc (ignoring its thickness). It has been found empirically [3] that the ε-length of an arc can often be approximated by a negative exponential function of ε, of the form $L_\varepsilon = K\varepsilon^{-d}$, where $d \geq 0$; here, $d = 0$ for straight lines, while d is of the order of 0.25 for very "wiggly" curves. (Thus, d can be used as a measure of straightness; alternatively, one can use the ratio between the length of the arc and the length of its chord as a simple measure of straightness.)

EXERCISE 1. What is the ε-length of the circumference of a circle as a function of ε?

> On integral-geometric methods for measuring area and perimeter by analyzing the intersections of a family of lines with the given subset, see the beginning of the next section. It can also be shown that the perimeter of a *convex* subset is just $\pi/2$ times the average length of its projection on a straight line.

b. *Distance Properties*

One can trivially measure the height or width of a picture subset as the distance between the highest and lowest horizontal lines, or rightmost and leftmost vertical lines, that meet the subset. Similarly, one can measure the *extent* of a subset in any given direction; for an example of the use of extent in pattern recognition, see [4]. The greatest extent of a subset (i.e., the greatest distance between any pair of points in it) is called its *diameter*.

EXERCISE 2. What is the average extent of the ellipse $x^2/a^2 + y^2/b^2 \leq 1$?

A less trivial problem is that of defining the length and width of an elongated subset. The following methods (see [20, 21], Section 8.4) are reasonable if the subset is relatively straight:

1. Let I be the principal axis of the subset; define the length of the subset as its extent in the direction parallel to I, and its width as its extent in the direction perpendicular to I.
2. Let R be the rectangle of the smallest area that can be circumscribed about the subset, and define the length and width of the subset as the lengths of the long and short sides of R.

A more general definition of length and width, which is also applicable to curved elongated subsets S, can be formulated as follows: Let S_d be the

159

area of the set of points of S that are at distance d, or greater, from $\bar{S}$. Evidently S_d is a decreasing function of d, and has dropped to zero by the time d reaches half the diameter of the S. If S has fairly constant width W, then S_d should drop to zero fairly abruptly as d reaches $W/2$. One could thus define the width of a S as twice the value of d (if any) for which S_d drops abruptly to a near zero value; one could then define the length of S to be its area divided by its width.

EXERCISE 3. What is S_d for an ellipse (together with its interior)?

A point pattern is determined "up to congruence" by specifying the distances between all pairs of its points; in fact, if there are more than three points, one need not even specify all of these distances to determine the pattern Equivalently: A polygon is determined "up to congruence" by specifying the lengths of (some of) its sides and diagonals. If a picture subset is approximated by a polygon, one can thus use interpoint distances, or combinations of them, as properties of the subset; see e.g., [5].

★EXERCISE 4. How many diagonals must be fixed, in addition to the sides, in order to determine an n-sided polygon "up to congruence"?

REFERENCES

1. H. Freeman, Techniques for the digital computer analysis of chain-encoded arbitrary plane curves, *Proc. Nat. Electron. Confer.* pp. 421–432 (October 1961).
2. J. Perkal, On the ε-length, *Bull. Acad. Polon. Sci., Classe III* 4, 399–403 (1956).
3. B. Mandelbrot, How long is the coast of Britain? Statistical self-similarity and fractional dimension, *Science* 156, 636–638 (May 5, 1967).
4. T. Marill and D. M. Green, Statistical recognition functions and the design of pattern recognizers, *IRE Trans. Electronic Computers* EC-9, 472–477 (December 1960).
5. W. Bungé, "Theoretical Geography." Gleerup Publishers, Lund, Sweden, 1962.

9.3. Metric Properties: Shape

a. Properties Defined Using Families of Subsets

Let $\mathscr{A}$ be a set of subsets of the plane (e.g., the set of all lines, the set of all horizontal lines, the set of all triples of points, etc.). Let $\mathfrak{F}$ be any geometrical property, and for each A in $\mathscr{A}$, compute the value of $\mathfrak{F}$ for the intersection $S \cap A$ of A with a given subset S. Then one can define new geometrical properties of S, in terms of $\mathfrak{F}$ and $\mathscr{A}$, by taking various statistics of the frequency distribution of the values of $\mathfrak{F}(S \cap A)$. This is the general concept that underlies the use of *integral geometry* in defining geometrical properties.

As an example, let $\mathscr{A}$ be the set of all lines; in particular let $L(p, \theta)$ be the line at perpendicular distance p from the origin, where the perpendicular makes angle θ with the x axis. If we compute the mean of $\mathfrak{F}(S \cap L(p, \theta))$, i.e., $\iint \mathfrak{F}(S \cap L(p, \theta))\, dp\, d\theta$, where $\mathfrak{F}(S \cap L(p, \theta))$ is the length of $S \cap L(p, \theta)$, it can be shown that we obtain π times the *area* of S; when $\mathfrak{F}$ is the connectivity of $S \cap L(p, \theta)$, we get the *perimeter* of S; while taking $\mathfrak{F} = 1$ if $L(p, \theta)$ meets S and $F = 0$ otherwise gives the *perimeter of the convex hull* of S [1, 2].

EXERCISE 1. Verify these assertions if S is an ellipse (together with its interior).

Another useful class of properties is obtained if we take $\mathscr{A}$ to be a set of n-tuples of points [3]. For example, let $n = 2$, and let $\mathfrak{F} = 1$ if both points lie in S, and $\mathfrak{F} = 0$ otherwise; then the mean of $\mathfrak{F}$ taken over all point pairs a given distance apart is just the property described at the end of Chapter 7. Similarly, if we use triples of collinear points, we can obtain a measure of the "degree of convexity" of S by using an $\mathfrak{F}$ that detects whether the two outer points lie in S but the intermediate point does not.

b. Local Properties

The criteria described in Section 8.4 for breaking the edge of a subset into pieces—position extrema, points of inflection, curvature maxima, etc.—can also be used to define properties of the given subset. For example, one can use the numbers (and positions, in the picture or along the subset's border) of position extrema, concavities ("loops"), curvature maxima ("angles"), or branches as properties; see, e.g., [4–7].

c. Complexity Properties

In studies of visual perception it has been found [8–10] that the judged complexity of an object is related to such properties as (1) the number of "angles" (i.e., curvature maxima in the object's edge), and the variability of the sizes of these angles; (2) P^2/A, the square of the object's perimeter divided by its area (the numerator is squared in order to make the quotient independent of the size of the object); note that this is smallest (equal to 4π) for a circle. These properties are evidently not entirely independent of one another, but neither are they completely redundant. If an object is "star-shaped" (i.e., every point of its boundary can be "seen" from some given interior point P), it can be completely described by specifying a single-valued function $r = r(\theta)$ that gives the equation of its boundary in polar coordinates with origin at P. In this case the variance of $r(\theta)$ [i.e., $\int (r(\theta) - \bar{r})^2 \, d\theta$, where $\bar{r} = \int r(\theta) \, d\theta$ is the average of $r(\theta)$] can be taken as a measure of complexity [11]; note that this too is smallest (equal to 0) for a circle.

EXERCISE 2. Show that a convex subset is star-shaped from any of its points.

EXERCISE 3. Compute P^2/A and the variance of $r(\theta)$ for the ellipse $x^2/a^2 + y^2/b^2 = 1$.

The foregoing complexity measures are appropriate if the given subset is a simply connected "shape." At the opposite extreme, suppose that the subset is a "pattern" consisting of many scattered points or lines. In this case one can take the *randomness* of the pattern as a measure of its complexity. Randomness can be defined, for point patterns, in terms of the variability of the number of points in a given neighborhood of each point, or the variability of the distances to a given number of nearest neighbors of each point [12, 13].

★ EXERCISE 4. Compute, for the random picture of Exercise 2, Section 6.1, (a) the variance of the number of elements in a neighborhood of each element, as a function of the size of the neighborhood; (b) the variance of the distance from each element to its nearest neighbor.

Symmetry is also evidently related to complexity. Given any picture subset, one can define its asymmetry relative to a given line or point in various ways; e.g., as $\iint |f(x, y) - f(x', y')| \, dx \, dy$, where f is the characteristic function of the subset and (x', y') is the point symmetric to (x, y) with respect to the given line or point. One can then define an *axis* (or *center*) of symmetry of the subset as a line or point relative to which the asymmetry is minimal.

★ EXERCISE 5. For the same picture as in Exercise 4, compute the asymmetry about the center of the picture and about the vertical line through the center of the picture.

EXERCISE 6. Compute the asymmetry of the ellipse $x^2/a^2 + y^2/b^2 = 1$ about the line $y = mx$. Do the same for the set of points (ki, kj), where $1 \leq i \leq n$ and $1 \leq j \leq n$.

REFERENCES

1. H. Steinhaus, Length, shape and area, *Colloq. Math.* **3**, 1–13 (1954).
2. A. B. J. Novikoff, Integral geometry as a tool in pattern perception, "Principles of Self-Organization " (H. von Foerster and G. W. Zopf, Jr., eds.), pp. 347–368. Pergamon Press, New York, 1962.
3. H. L. Frisch and B. Julesz, Figure-ground perception and random geometry, *Perception Psychophys.* **1**, 389–398 (1966).
4. W. Sprick and K. Ganzhorn, An analogous method for pattern recognition by following the boundary, *Proc. Intern. Confer. Inform. Process., UNESCO, Paris, 1959* pp. 238–244. UNESCO, Paris, 1960.
5. H. Kazmierczak, The potential field as an aid to character recognition, *ibid.* pp. 244–247. UNESCO, Paris, 1960.
6. L. D. Harmon, A line-drawing pattern recognizer, *WJCC* pp. 351–364 (May 1960).
7. L. D. Harmon, Line-drawing pattern recognizer, *Electronics* **33**, 39–43 (September 2, 1960).
8. F. Attneave, Physical determinants of the judged complexity of shapes, *J. Exptl. Psychol.* **53**, 221–227 (1957).
9. M. D. Arnoult, Prediction of perceptual responses from structural characteristics of the stimulus, *Perceptual Motor Skills* **11**, 261–268 (1960).
10. H. H. Stenson, The physical structure of random forms and their judged complexity, *Perception Psychophys.* **1**, 303–310 (1966).
11. R. R. Boyce and W. A. V. Clark, The concept of shape in geography, *Geograph. Rev.* **54**, 561–572 (1964).
12. M. F. Dacey and T. H. Tung, The identification of randomness in point patterns, *J. Reg. Sci.* **4**, 83–96 (1962).
13. M. F. Dacey, Description of line patterns, "Quantitative Geography " (W. L. Garrison and D. F. Marble, eds.), pp. 279–287. Dept. of Geography, Northwestern Univ., Evanston, Illinois, 1967.

9.4. Functions of Picture Subsets

a. *Equations*

Any picture subset is completely determined by specifying its edge as a set of directed curves.† Thus, the subset can be described by giving the equa-

---

† If the subset is simply connected, only one curve is needed; but if it has several connected components, or if it has holes, additional curves are required. The directions of the curves should be chosen consistently so that the subset lies to the left of each curve.

tions of these curves. For example, as pointed out in Section 9.3, if a subset is "star shaped" from some point P, it can be completely described by specifying the distance from P to each point on its edge—in other words, the equation of its edge in polar coordinates with P as origin. (This description can be made independent of orientation, e.g., by expanding it in a Fourier series and taking the modulus; and of scale, e.g., by dividing by the diameter of the subset.) In particular two subsets can be matched by matching their edge curves. As pointed out in Section 8.3, this requires only one dimensional cross correlation, rather than the two dimensional cross correlation needed to match the subsets themselves. In fact if the equations are normalized (e.g., as just described), the problem can be reduced to one of simple template matching.

An important method of describing the edge of a subset is by its *intrinsic equation*, which gives its curvature as a function of arc length (measured from any starting point). This equation completely determines the edge "up to congruence"; and it too can be made independent of size and of starting point. (One way of doing the latter is to start from some specific, identifiable point, e.g., a point at which the curvature is greatest.) Alternatively, one can use the slope, rather than curvature, of the edge as a function of arc length; this is, of course, not independent of orientation. Still another useful "equation" is provided by taking the angle between the radius vector (i.e., the line from the origin) to a point of the edge and the tangent to the edge at that point as a function of arc length; this can also be shown to be independent of position, orientation, and scale [1].

EXERCISE 1. What is the intrinsic equation of an ellipse, starting from one end of the major axis?

The "chain encoding" of an arc as a sequence of steps of a given length in one of a given set of directions can be thought of as a discrete "intrinsic equation," since it gives (quantized) slope as a function of (quantized) arc length. Moreover, if differences of successive slopes are taken, it gives a quantized "curvature" (i.e., rate of change of slope) as a function of arc length ([2, 3]; compare [4]).

b. *Frequency Distributions*

Frequency distributions of the values of subset properties provide a variety of useful one parameter functions. Two examples are (1) the distribution of slopes (or curvatures, etc.) of the subset's edge (on this "directionality spectrum," see [2, 3]); and (2) the distribution of distances from the subset (or edge of the subset) to itself (see [5]).

c. Functions Defined Using Families of Subsets†

Let $\mathscr{A}$ be a one-parameter family of subsets A_λ of the plane (e.g., the set of all lines with a given slope); then, for any picture subset property $\mathfrak{F}$, $\mathfrak{F}(S \cap A_\lambda)$ gives us a function of λ for any given subset S. For a wide variety of functions of this type see, e.g., [6–11], as well as [7], Section 7.2.

Similarly, let $\mathscr{A}$ be a two- (or more) parameter family of subsets (e.g., the set of all lines), so that $\mathfrak{F}(S \cap A)$ (where A is in $\mathscr{A}$) is a function of two or more parameters; if we compute statistics with respect to all but one of these parameters, the result is a function of a single parameter. For example, let $\mathscr{A}$ be the set of all lines, and compute the average of $\mathfrak{F}(S \cap A)$ over all lines having a given slope; then the result is a function of slope. See, e.g., [12], as well as [1–3] in Section 8.4.

EXERCISE 2. Let $\mathscr{A}$ be the set of all lines that intersect the ellipse $x^2/a^2 + y^2/b^2 \le 1$. What is the average length of the intersection taken over all lines in $\mathscr{A}$ that have slope m?

REFERENCES

1. J. W. Brouillette and C. W. Johnson, Pattern recognition, *Proc. 4th Nat. Conv. Military Electron.* pp. 179–182 (June 1960).
2. H. Freeman, A technique for the classification and recognition of geometric patterns, *Proc. 3rd Intern. Congr. Cybernetics* (*September* 1961) pp. 348–369. Association Internationale de Cybernétique, Namur, Belgium, 1965.
3. H. Freeman, On the digital computer classification of geometrical line patterns, *Proc. Nat. Electron. Confer.* pp. 312–324 (October 1962).
4. T. Sugiura and T. Higashiuwatoko, A method for the recognition of Japanese hiragana characters, *IEEE Trans. Information Theory* **IT-14**, 226–233 (March 1968).
5. J. A. Deutsch, A theory of shape recognition, *Brit. J. Psychol.* **46**, 30–37 (1955); reprinted in PR, pp. 177–184.
6. W. Doyle, Recognition of sloppy, hand-printed characters, *WJCC* pp. 133–142 (May 1960).

† Compare Section 9.3a.

7. M. Nadler, Une systeme analogique-digital pour la reconnaissance de caracteres, "Information Processing 1962" (C. M. Popplewell, ed.), pp. 456–461. North-Holland, Amsterdam, 1963.

Compare M. Nadler, An analog-digital character recognition system, *IEEE Trans. Electronic Computers* **EC-12**, 814–821 (December 1963).

8. S. B. Akers and B. H. Rutter, The use of threshold logic in character recognition, *Proc. IEEE* **52**, 931–938 (August 1964).

9. J. E. Rubio, The clustering and recognition of patterns, *Intern. J. Control* **4**, 459–485 (1966).

10. T. Pavlidis, Computer recognition of figures through decomposition, *Information and Control* **12**, 526–537 (May-June 1968).

11. T. Pavlidis, On the syntactic analysis of figures, *Proc. ACM Nat. Confer.* pp. 183–188 (August 1968).

12. J. P. Latham, Methodology for an instrumented geographic analysis, *Ann. Assoc. Amer. Geographers* **53**, 194–209 (June 1963).

See also J. P. Latham and R. E. Witmer, Comparative waveform analysis of multisensor imagery, *Photogrammetric Engrg.* **33**, 779–786 (July 1967).

CHAPTER 10

Picture Description and Picture Languages

As pointed out at the beginning of Chapter 7, the general problem of pictorial pattern recognition involves not merely the classification, but the *description*, of given pictures. Typically, a picture description refers to picture properties (as measured over the entire picture or over subsets); to geometrical subset properties; and to such *relationships* between subsets as "above," "to the left of," "near," "between," "inside of," "part of," "larger than," "darker than," etc.

Just as a subset property is a real-valued function defined on the set of all subsets, so a binary relation between subsets is a real-valued function defined on the set of all pairs of subsets. Analogously for ternary and higher-order relations, using the set of all triples, etc., of subsets; however, these are rare in practice. Many important properties and relations (including all of the above examples, if we assume that they have been precisely defined) are binary-valued, being either true or false for a given (pair of) subsets; but this can be regarded as a special case of real-valuedness. ("Properties" and "relations" whose values are functions of one or more parameters will not be considered here.)

Given a set of such properties and relationships, it becomes possible, in principle, to generate a description of the picture in words, answer questions about the picture, and determine whether given "configurations" (i.e., combinations of subsets having given properties and standing in given relationships) are present in the picture.

If the picture to be described is simple, e.g., if it is made up of simple geometrical figures, each having a constant gray level, it is not difficult to extract from it all the information that would normally be required for its description. For such pictures, even a "complete" description (i.e., one from which the picture can be reconstructed exactly) can usually be obtained. In all but the simplest cases, however, the required information may be very hard to extract. In fact the desired description may require information that does not correspond to any measurable property of the picture itself, but rather that is inferred by the observer on the basis of prior knowledge about the given class of pictures, or about the objects that they depict. To obtain adequate picture descriptions in such cases, a model of the class of pictures (and/or objects) is needed; such a model can be used as a guide in analyzing the picture, and as a basis for making inferences about it.

In this chapter we discuss "languages" that can be used to describe various types of pictures and their application to the specification of models for particular classes of pictures. Languages for the manipulation of synthetic pictures, such as those which have been developed for use in various computer graphics systems, will not be considered.

> For a recent example, which also incorporates a limited capability for analyzing pictures, see H. E. Kulsrud, A general purpose graphic language, *Comm. ACM* **11**, 247–254 (April 1968).

10.1. Picture Description Languages

Given a set of properties of and relations among a set of entities, one wants to store this information in a compact, well-organized form, so that it can be efficiently searched if it is desired to answer questions or locate specified "configurations." Various types of "data structures" have been developed [1] for such purposes. Many of these structures were designed for storing descriptions of line drawings in computer graphics systems [2]; typically, they are designed to handle only a limited number of types of entities (here, picture subsets), properties, or relations. Since the subject of data structures is not specific to picture processing (or even to computer graphics), it will not be discussed further. In the following paragraphs we describe various "languages" (a more suggestive term might be "notations") that are specifically designed for describing pictures. (Languages capable of "complete" descriptions, from which the pictures can be reconstructed, will be discussed in Section 10.2.)

a. *Description of Line Drawings*

Much of the work on picture description languages has dealt with line drawings. Segmentation is usually relatively easy for such pictures, and the resulting subsets (arcs and curves) can be compactly represented by chain encoding (Sections 3.4a and 9.4a). Given a line drawing, one can identify in it various types of "vertices" (e.g., angles, points of inflection, nodes, etc.; see Section 8.4). One can then describe the drawing as consisting of "vertices," some of which are joined by arcs. A partial metric description of the arcs themselves can be given in terms of such properties as mean slope, straightness, length, etc.; or one can even discard the metric information entirely and describe the drawing topologically, by specifying the number of arcs joining each pair of vertices [3–7].

As an example of this type of description, consider the drawing shown in Figure 10.1. Here A, D, and E are angles, while B and C are nodes. If we take

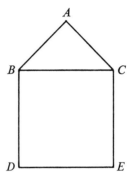

Figure 10.1. Simple line-drawing figure.

all five of these points as vertices, we can describe the topology of the drawing by a triangular matrix of the form

$$
\begin{array}{c|cccc}
 & A & B & C & D \\
\hline
B & 1 \\
C & 1 & 1 \\
D & 0 & 1 & 0 \\
E & 0 & 0 & 1 & 1 \\
\end{array}
$$

where a "1" indicates that the vertex at the head of its column is joined by a single arc to the vertex at the head of its row. (Note that if we had just used the nodes B and C as vertices, the matrix would reduce to

$$
\begin{array}{c|c}
 & B \\
\hline
C & 3 \\
\end{array}
$$

169

indicating that B and C are joined by three arcs; here, however, the arcs are not straight line segments, as they are if we use all five points as vertices.) The fact that B and C are nodes, while A, D, and E are angles, is represented in the matrix by the fact that B and C are on three arcs, while A, D, and E are on only two.

If a drawing has many vertices, the matrix representation of its topology becomes uneconomical, since typically only a few of the possible pairs of vertices will be joined by arcs, but the matrix must reserve space for every pair. We can avoid this by describing the "topology" of the drawing in a different way: For each vertex, we list the other vertices to which it is joined by arcs (for brevity, we shall call these other vertices its "neighbors"). For Figure 10.1, this type of description would be of the form

$$A(B, C); \ B(D, C, A); \ C(A, B, E); \ D(E, B); \ E(C, D)$$

(If there were more than one arc joining a pair of vertices, we could denote this by allowing repetitions on their neighbor lists.) Note that this description is symmetric in the sense that if Y is a neighbor of X, then X is a neighbor of Y. Note also that this form of description can be used to specify the *ordering* of the arcs at each vertex (we have listed them in counterclockwise order in the above example); this information is not available from the matrix description.

For most purposes, specifying the topology of a line drawing does not constitute an adequate description; metric information is also needed. As previously indicated, examples of such information are lengths and mean slopes of arcs. From this information, other useful metric properties can be derived. For example, the mean angle between two arcs can be obtained by subtracting their slopes. (Here and above, if the arcs are always straight line segments, as they are in our example, the word "mean" can be omitted.) One can indicate that two line segments have the same length, without having to specify what that length is, by representing their slopes by the same ("variable") symbol; the same method can be used to indicate that two segments are parallel (i.e., have the same slope), perpendicular (i.e. have slopes differing by 90°), etc.

The following is a set of possible metric data for Figure 10.1; the notation is self-explanatory:

LENGTH $(A, B) = x$	LENGTH $(B, C) = y$	LENGTH $(D, E) = y$
LENGTH $(A, C) = x$	LENGTH $(C, E) = y$	LENGTH $(B, D) = y$
SLOPE $(B, C) = \theta$	SLOPE $(D, B) = \theta + 90$	SLOPE $(B, A) = \theta + 45$
SLOPE $(D, E) = \theta$	SLOPE $(E, C) = \theta + 90$	SLOPE $(C, A) = \theta + 135$

(We could have also indicated that $x = y/\sqrt{2}$; if necessary, we could have also explicitly indicated that the "arcs" are all straight lines by giving STRAIGHTNESS data for each of them.) Note that we have not specified y or θ, nor have we specified the position of the drawing. Thus the above metric description is independent of position, orientation, and scale—it determines the drawing only "up to similarity."† Note also that the information given above is redundant; e.g., the slope information already tells us that $BCDE$ is a rectangle and that ABC is an isosceles right triangle, so that we need only specify the equality of either pair of adjacent sides of $BCDE$ to complete the description. It should be pointed out that the drawing can be completely reconstructed "up to similarity" (and if we specify the value of x, even "up to congruence") from this description. In other words, although, in general, the descriptions provided by this notation are only partial, for drawings made up of straight lines, they can actually be complete.

EXERCISE 1. What would we know about the drawing if we had only the length information?

EXERCISE 2. Write topological and metric descriptions, similar to those given above, for each of the following line drawings: (a) a right triangle, (b) an equilateral triangle, (c) a trapezoid, (d) a parallelogram, (e) a rectangle, (f) a rhombus, (g) a square, (h) a square with its diagonals, and (i) a regular hexagon. Which of these descriptions determines its drawing "up to similarity"?

b. *Description of Relationships among Picture Subsets*

Another class of picture description languages is concerned primarily with the description of geometrical relationships among picture subsets rather than with the structures of the individual subsets ([8–10]; compare [11]). Typically, such languages deal with pictures containing easily "nameable" subsets, such as simple geometrical figures.

For the drawing in Figure 10.1, a very simple partial description of the example considered above might take some such form as "ONTOP (right triangle, square)," indicating that the drawing contains two subsets (the right triangle and the square) between which the relation ONTOP holds. A more

† If the drawing were not connected, we would have to give some sort of relative position information about its connected components in order to determine its shape "up to similarity." (Another way to do this would be to add "invisible arcs" to it and specify their lengths and slopes.)

complex example is provided by Figure 10.2. Here a (self-explanatory) partial description might take the form

SQUARE (a)	RECTANGLE (b)	
SQUARE (c)	RECTANGLE (e)	
SQUARE (d)		
LEFT (a, b)	CONGRUENT (a, c)	BETWEEN (b; a, c)
LEFT (b, c)	LARGER (d, a)	NEARER (b; c, a)
ABOVE (b, d)	TALLER (b, d)	NEARER (b; d, c)
INSIDE (e, d)	WIDER (e, b)	

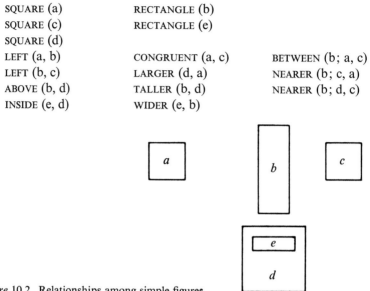

Figure 10.2. Relationships among simple figures.

Ideally, one would want a description language to be "large enough" to accommodate *any* statement (or question, or command) that one might reasonably wish to utter about pictures, or, at least, about pictures of some given type. A series of languages for the description of photomicrographs of nervous tissue has been developed [12] that is eventually intended to provide this capability.

REFERENCES

1. J. C. Gray, Compound data structures for computer aided design: a survey, *Proc. ACM Nat. Confer.* pp. 355–365 (August 1967).
2. M. D. Prince, Man-computer graphics for computer-aided design, *Proc. IEEE* **54**, 1698–1708 (December 1966).
3. T. Marill, A. K. Hartley, T. G. Evans, B. H. Bloom, D. M. R. Park, T. P. Hart, and D. L. Darley, CYCLOPS-1: a second-generation recognition system, *FJCC* pp. 27–33 (December 1963).

4. B. H. Bloom and T. Marill, CYCLOPS-2: a computer system that learns to see, AD 624152 (October 1965).

5. T. Marill and B. H. Bloom, Learning and perceptual processes for computers, *Ann. New York Acad. Sci.* **128**, 1029–1034. (January 1966).

6. A. Guzman, Scene analysis using the concept of model, AD 652017 (January 1967).

7. A. Guzman, Some aspects of pattern recognition by computer, AD 656041 (February 1967).

8. R. F. Simmons, Answering English questions by computer: a survey, *Comm. ACM* **8**, 53–70 (January 1965).

9. D. L. Londe and R. F. Simmons, NAMER: a pattern-recognition system for generating sentences about relations between line drawings, *Proc. ACM Nat. Confer.* pp. 162–175 (August 1965).

10. M. Kochen, Automatic question-answering of English-like questions about simple diagrams, *J. ACM* **16**, 26–48 (January 1969).

11. T. G. Evans, A heuristic program to solve geometric-analogy problems, *SJCC* pp. 327–338 (April 1964).

   See also T. G. Evans, A program for the solution of a class of geometric-analogy intelligence-test questions, AD 609845 (November 1964).

12. L. E. Lipkin, W. C. Watt, and R. A. Kirsch, The analysis, synthesis and description of biological images, *Ann. New York Acad. Sci.* **128**, 984–1012 (January 1966).

10.2. Picture Languages

If a picture description language is capable of expressing complete descriptions, from which pictures can be exactly reconstructed, it can be regarded as defining a "picture language," in which one can specify how pictures are built up out of pieces (presumably corresponding to parts of the description) in various ways, just as phrases and sentences are built up by concatenating words. The pieces of pictures used as building blocks in a language of this type can range from single picture elements to complex geometrical figures; naturally, the more "primitive" the elements are, the more general is the class of pictures that can be built up, but the more complicated are the descriptions of the pictures in terms of the pieces.

To illustrate how a picture can be built up by combining pieces, we describe one way of building up Figure 10.1 out of the four pieces shown in Figure 10.3a. Here H and T can be thought of as the "head" and "tail," respectively; if we did not distinguish these, there would be no way of distinguishing between the two combinations in Figure 10.3b. (The "heads" and "tails"

173

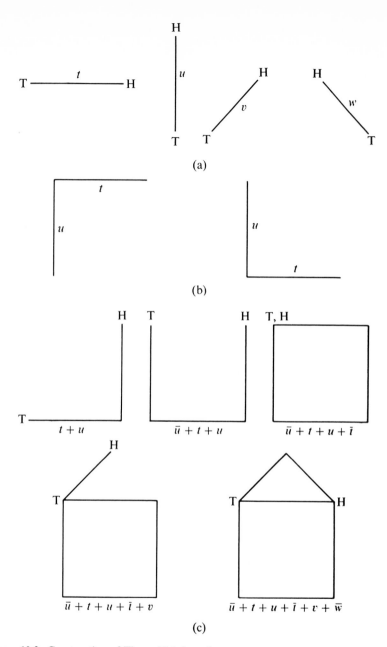

Figure 10.3. Construction of Figure 10.1 from line segments. (a) The line segments. (b) Two combinations of the line segments. (c) Steps in the construction.

174

of words need not be explicitly designated when we use them to build up sentences, since the way in which they are to be put together is completely determined by specifying their sequence.) If x, y are any two "pieces," let $\bar{x}$ ("the reversal of x") denote x with its head and tail interchanged, and let $x + y$ denote the "composite piece" obtained by putting x and y together head to tail (i.e., the head of x touching the tail of y), where the tail of x becomes the tail of $x + y$, and the head of y becomes the head of $x + y$. In this notation the two combinations in Figure 10.3b can be specified as

$$u + t \quad \text{and} \quad \bar{u} + t$$

respectively. Note that the $+$ operation is *associative*, i.e., $(x + y) + z$ yields the same figure as $x + (y + z)$. The steps in building up Figure 10.1 out of the four pieces, using the $+$ and reversal operations, are shown in Figure 10.3c.

EXERCISE 1. In how many different ways can a square be built up out of the pieces t and u using these operations?

> In the construction shown in Figure 10.3, the fact that a closed square is formed at the third step and a closed triangle at the last step are not explicit in the description. When we put $\bar{u} + t + u$ head to tail with $\bar{t}$, they also come together tail to head, but the description does not show this. This defect can be overcome by introducing an additional operation that explicitly stipulates that two pieces are put together head to tail and tail to head (such as operation could, of course, be applied only if the figures "fit").

EXERCISE 2. Give a construction for Figure 10.1 in which a "head to tail and tail to head" operation is allowed.

The method of constructing pictures just described can be generalized to allow still other "composition" operations, as well as additional "attachment points" (besides "head" and "tail"). In general a composition operation is defined by specifying which attachment points of the elements are to be brought into coincidence, and which of them are to become the attachment points of the new (composite) element. Note that an infinite set of pictures can be built up out of a finite set of pieces in this way, since the composition operations can be used arbitrary numbers of times.

EXERCISE 3. Give constructions for the capital letters A, E, F, H, K, and L using straight-line segments as pieces, and (a) allowing, (b) not allowing "middle" attachment points.

EXERCISE 4. Give a construction for the letters B, C, D, O, P, Q, and S using straight-line segments and arcs of circles as pieces.

The pictures that can be built up using such methods need not be line drawings; we can similarly build up pictures of "solid" objects out of "solid" pieces. For example, suppose that we take as our basic "piece" a solid square with three attachment points (Figure 10.4) and define two composition operations $+_U$ and $+_V$ as follows: In $x +_U y$ we combine the elements x and y by making H_x coincide with U_y and taking $H_{x +_U y} = H_y$, $U_{x +_U y} = U_x$, $V_{x +_U y} = V_y$; similarly, in $x +_V y$ we make H_x coincide with V_y, and take $H_{x +_V y} = H_y$, $U_{x +_V y} = U_y$, and $V_{x +_V y} = V_x$. (These two operations evidently "attach" x to y on the left and below, respectively.) We can construct a 2-by-2 solid square, using these operations, in various ways, e.g., $x +_U [(x +_U x) +_V x]$.

EXERCISE 5. In how many different ways can this construction be done?

If the "pieces" used in a picture language have only two attachment points each, the language can be regarded as being essentially one-dimensional, since (as in Figure 10.3) the description of any picture built up out of these pieces consists of a *string* of elements.

The methods of constructing pictures described in this section provide an important general approach to the problem of pictorial pattern recognition. Let $\mathscr{F}$ be a set of pictures that can be built up out of a given set of pieces using given composition operations, and suppose that we are given an unknown picture f belonging to $\mathscr{F}$; then we can identify f if we can identify the pieces in it and the way in which they are combined. Evidently, for this approach to be advantageous, the pieces should be relatively simple, and thus easier to recognize than are the pictures themselves (we certainly should not, in general, use entire pictures as "pieces"!). On the other hand, if the pieces are too simple, very complex combinations of them may be required in order to build up the pictures, so that the recognition of these combinations becomes

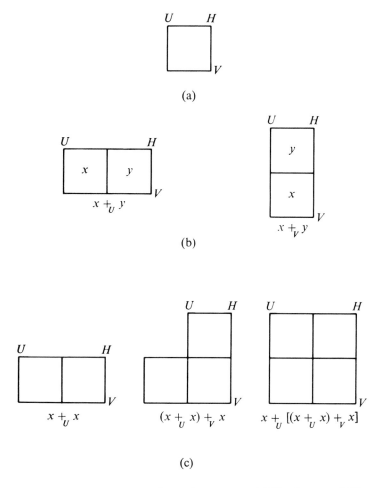

Figure 10.4. Construction of a 2-by-2 square from 1-by-1 squares. (a) The elements. (b) The operations $+_U$ and $+_V$. (c) Steps in the construction of a 2-by-2 square.

complicated. This difficulty can be minimized by using a hierarchical approach in which very simple pieces are combined to yield simple "subpictures"; these in turn are combined to yield less simple ones; and so on until the pictures in $\mathscr{F}$ are obtained.

If the pictures of interest are line drawings, *chain encoding* provides a systematic method of building them up out of very simple pieces, namely, straight line segments of "unit length" in the principal directions (multiples of 45°). (Note that the diagonally oriented "unit" segments are $\sqrt{2}$ as long as those oriented horizontally or vertically.) A natural approach to constructing Figure 10.1, starting from such unit segements, is to first use them to build up the four "pieces" t, u, v, w of Figure 10.3a, and then use these in turn to construct Figure 10.1 as shown in Figure 10.3c; this illustrates the hierarchical concept suggested above. In general, given a line drawing, one can break it down into vertices joined by arcs, as described in Section 10.1a, and can then describe the arcs by specifying their chain encodings.

EXERCISE 6. Carry out the construction of Figure 10.1 by the method just described. Assume that the square is six units on a side.

EXERCISE 7. What is the chain encoding of a straight-line segment of slope 60°?

EXERCISE 8. Apply Exercise 7 to give a hierarchical construction for an equilateral triangle based on chain encoding.

★ EXERCISE 9. Characterize the chain encodings that represent straight-line segments.

More generally, arbitrary digital pictures containing "solid" objects can be built up using unit squares (having various gray levels) as elements. Here again, it is advantageous to do this stepwise, i.e., by first combining the unit squares into larger "blocks," or into "edge segments" in the principal directions, and then combining these into still larger "blobs," "edges," etc.

EXERCISE 10. Construct a "solid" digital version of Figure 10.1 using unit squares as pieces. Use the same dimensions as in Exercise 6. [*Hint*: You may need to introduce additional composition operations.]

REFERENCES

1. R. A. Kirsch, Computer interpretation of English text and picture patterns, *IEEE Trans. Electronic Computers* **EC-13**, 363–376 (August 1964).
2. M. B. Clowes, An hierarchical model of form perception, MPSVF, pp. 388–398.

3. M. B. Clowes, Perception, picture processing and computers, "Machine Intelligence 1" (N. L. Collins and D. Michie, eds.), pp. 181–197. American Elsevier, New York, 1967.
4. M. B. Clowes, Pictorial relationships—a syntactic approach, "Machine Intelligence 4" (B. Meltzer and D. Michie, eds.), pp. 361–383. American Elsevier, New York, 1969.
5. M. B. Clowes, Transformational grammars and the organization of pictures, "Automatic Interpretation and Classification of Images" (A. Grasselli, ed.). Academic Press, New York, in press, 1969.
6. J. Feder, Languages of encoded line patterns, *Information and Control* **13**, 230–244 (September 1968).
7. W. F. Miller and A. C. Shaw, Linguistic methods in picture processing—a survey, *FJCC* pp. 279–290 (December 1968).

10.3. Models for Classes of Pictures

Given a language for describing pictures, whether partially or completely, one can use it to formulate definitions for specific classes of pictures. For example, as seen in Section 10.1a, a language for describing line drawings in terms of "vertices" and the arcs joining them can be used to characterize various simple types of geometrical figures, e.g., simple closed polygons (all vertices are "angles," all arcs are straight-line segments), parallelograms (quadrilaterals whose pairs of nonconsecutive sides are equal), etc. Similarly, as indicated in Section 10.2 (see Exercises 3 and 4), definitions for alphabetic characters can be given in terms of a suitable set of "strokes" (see [18], Section 5.1, as well as [1–6].)

In all of these cases the pictures are completely stylized; the definitions of the characters describe only specific examples of the characters. A more difficult task is that of defining *nonstylized* characters. Since the number of different ways of writing an acceptable character is extremely large, it is impractical to define the characters by describing every possible example; and the same is certainly true for classes of pictures more complex than characters. However, one can attempt to give definitions in such cases by formulating restrictions on the allowable combinations of "pieces." For example, one can attempt to define characters by using restrictions on the combinations of unit segments that make up the "strokes," and on the combinations of strokes that make up the characters.

This approach, in which a class of acceptable pictures is defined by restricting the way in which sets of pieces can be combined, is analogous to the approach used in mathematical linguistics, where a class of acceptable (i.e., "grammatical") sentences is defined by specifying grammatical rules that

179

restrict the way in which words can be concatenated. In the following paragraphs we review some basic concepts of mathematical linguistics, and indicate how they can be generalized to "picture languages."

Consider the set of words

a, and, another, boy, girl, hears, sees

These words can be combined into "statements" in many ways, but only a few of these combinations will be grammatical English sentences. We can restrict the allowable combinations, so that only grammatical sentences are obtained, by formulating grammatical rules such as the following (here the vertical line is short for " or "):

ARTICLE = a | another
NOUN = boy | girl
VERB = hears | sees
NOUNPHRASE = ARTICLE NOUN
COMPOUNDPHRASE = NOUNPHRASE | NOUNPHRASE and COMPOUNDPHRASE
SENTENCE = NOUNPHRASE VERB COMPOUNDPHRASE

In this "grammar" there is only one composition operation, namely concatenation (e.g., ARTICLE NOUN means "ARTICLE followed by NOUN"). The combinations of words that can be constructed using these rules will all be grammatical sentences. For example, we can construct the sentence "a boy sees another girl and a boy" as follows:

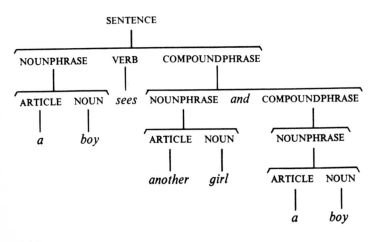

Note that an infinite number of sentences can be constructed using this grammar, since the rule

COMPOUNDPHRASE = NOUNPHRASE and COMPOUNDPHRASE

can be used repeatedly to yield arbitrarily long sequences of NOUNPHRASES connected by "ands."

EXERCISE 1. Write out the construction for the sentence "another girl hears a girl and another boy and another girl" using this grammar.

★ EXERCISE 2. Show that the same set of sentences is obtained if we replace the last two rules of our grammar by the two rules

VERB NOUNPHRASE = VERB NOUNPHRASE and NOUNPHRASE
SENTENCE = NOUNPHRASE VERB NOUNPHRASE

(This revised grammar is now "context-sensitive" in the sense that it permits us to replace NOUNPHRASE by "NOUNPHRASE and NOUNPHRASE" only when it occurs in a certain "context"—specifically, when it is immediately preceded by VERB. A grammar of the type given in the text is called "context-free.")

★ EXERCISE 3. Write rules for a grammar, using the set of words "a, and, another, boy, girl, hears, sees, who," that allows the construction of such sentences as "a boy sees a girl and a boy who hears a girl and another girl who sees a girl."

There is an evident analogy between the rules of a grammar such as that just described and the construction of a picture out of pieces. To see this analogy more clearly, let us write a set of rules—"picture grammar"—that can be used to construct the drawing in Figure 10.1, where the square is six units long. We denote by $a, b, \ldots, g, h$ the "unit" line segments in the directions $0°, 45°, \ldots, 270°$, and $315°$, respectively.

$$t = a + a + a + a + a + a$$
$$u = c + c + c + c + c + c$$
$$\overline{t} = e + e + e + e + e + e$$
$$\overline{u} = g + g + g + g + g + g$$
$$v = b + b + b$$
$$\overline{w} = h + h + h$$
$$\text{SQUARE} = \overline{u} + t + u + \overline{t}$$
$$\text{TENT} = v + \overline{w}$$
$$\text{DRAWING} = \text{SQUARE} + \text{TENT}$$

181

Note that these rules yield only our one DRAWING, since they involve no "ors." However, it is easy to specify picture grammars that yield many, even infinitely many, drawings. For example,

$$\text{HORIZLINESEG} = a \mid \text{HORIZLINESEG} + a$$

yields horizontal line segments of all possible integer lengths. Similarly, using the notation of the solid-square example of Section 10.2, the picture grammar

$$\text{RECTANGLE} = x +_V x \mid \text{RECTANGLE} + (x +_V x)$$

yields all solid rectangles two units high and an integer number of units long. It is also possible (but more complicated) to write picture grammars that yield rectangles of all sizes; on the analogous problem for right triangles, see [1], Section 10.2.

The "grammatical" approach to picture construction illustrated by the foregoing examples provides a capability for describing large sets of pictures, using small sets of "pieces," and of grammatical rules. However, all of the examples given still involve only simple (and hence "stylized") geometrical figures. Moreover, they provide little insight into how one might go about writing picture grammars for broader classes of shapes—even for such simple ones as the class of hand-printed 0's, let alone such classes as "chromosomes" or "clouds." In addition little or no work has been done as yet on grammars for pictures involving shades of gray or visual textures.

If one is willing to start with relatively high-level "pieces," making no attempt to build these up from simpler pieces, it is possible to write grammars for "generalized" pictures made up of the given pieces; but the usefulness of these grammars for real-world pictorial pattern recognition depends on one's ability to recognize the pieces. The following is a very simple example of a grammar on this level:

$$\text{STICK} = \text{POINT} \mid \text{SIDE} + \text{STICK} + \text{SIDE}$$
$$\text{PENCIL} = \text{STICK} + \text{ERASER}$$

Here POINT presumably has a v-shape, SIDE is a straight-line segment of some unit length, and so on. The grammars mentioned earlier [1–6] for handprinted and handwritten characters in terms of strokes, and a grammar ([7]; see also [12], Section 8.2) for outlines of chromosomes, are other examples. These examples make use of only a single, concatenation-like composition operation

("+"); the following is a simple example of a grammar involving composition operations that represent other types of relationships among the pieces:

EYES = EYE (next to) EYE

FEATURES = EYES (above) NOSE (above) MOUTH

OUTLINE = EAR (alongside) HEAD (alongside) EAR

FACE = FEATURES (inside) OUTLINE

For another example (a grammar for constructing pictures of houses using the pieces "wall," "roof," "gable," "door," "window," and "chimney"), see [8]. Here, of course, the practical utility of such a grammar depends on our ability to recognize not only the pieces, but also the relationships represented by the composition operations, since these too are not precisely defined.

Given a grammar for a class of pictures, as well as a language (e.g., a subset of English) in which the pictures can be described, one can regard the picture description problem as one of "translation" from the picture language into the description language (see [12], Section 10.1). Such translation is relatively straightforward for a "high-level" picture language in which the elements and the composition operations all have simple verbal descriptions; but the situation is more complicated if one must start to build up from the level of individual picture elements, where in many cases (e.g., building up visual textures out of elements) verbalization is very difficult. Conventional grammars build up sentences out of words, which are relatively high-level units; a picture grammar for generating complex pictures starting from single picture elements would be analogous to a "grammar" for English that started from the individual "elements" of a digitized speech waveform. A further difficulty, which the problem of picture description shares with that of natural language translation, is that (as pointed out at the beginning of this chapter) one often requires information that is not actually present in the input, but that can be inferred on the basis of prior knowledge about the real-world objects being discussed or depicted. A truly general picture description system would thus have to incorporate not only a picture processing capability, but also a model for the reality that underlies the pictures. If we want to give our computers eyes, we must first give them an education in the facts of life.

REFERENCES

1. R. Narasimhan, On the description, generation and recognition of classes of pictures, "Automatic Interpretation and Classification of Images " (A. Grasselli, ed.). Academic Press, New York, in press, 1969.

2. M. Eden and M. Halle, The characterization of cursive writing, *Proc. 4th London Symp. Inform. Theory* pp. 287–299. Butterworth, London and Washington, D.C. 1961.
3. M. Eden, On the formalization of handwriting, *Proc. Symp. Appl. Math.* **12**, 83–88 (1961). Amer. Math. Soc., Providence, Rhode Island, 1961.
4. M. Eden, Handwriting and pattern recognition, *IRE Trans. Information Theory* **IT-8**, 160–166 (February 1962).
5. M. Eden, Handwriting generation and recognition, "Recognizing Patterns" (P. A. Kolers and M. Eden, eds.), pp. 138–154. M.I.T. Press, Cambridge, Massachusetts, 1968.
6. P. J. Knoke and R. G. Wiley, A linguistic approach to mechanical pattern recognition, *Proc. IEEE Comput. Confer.* pp. 142–144 (September 1967).
7. R. S. Ledley, High-speed automatic analysis of biomedical pictures, *Science* **146**, 216–223 (October 9, 1964).
8. R. S. Ledley, "Programming and Utilizing Digital Computers," pp. 364–367. McGraw-Hill, New York, 1962.

Author Index

Numbers in parentheses are reference numbers and indicate that an author's work is referred to, although his name is not cited in the text. Numbers in italics show the page on which the complete reference is listed. Numbers in brackets are cross references.

Subject Index

A

Acutance, 85
Additive noise, 75, 93
Approximation
  of line drawings, 29–31
  of pictures, 4, 19–33
Area, 158, 161
Autocorrelation, 40, 55–56, 86–87, 110–112, 123
  higher order, 111, 123
Averaging
  of multiple copies, 91–92
  over neighborhood, 88–91

B

Binary-valued picture, 2
Binary-valued property, 114–115
Bit, 8
Bit plane coding, 18
Block coding, 13–15
Border, 134
  following, 135–136, 137–138

C

Chain encoding, 30–31, 164, 177–178
Classification, 5, 105–106
Cluster, 143–144
Coding, 4, 7–18
Coherent light, 60–68
Color separation, 57–58
Complexity, 161–162

Composition operation, 175, 176, 182–183
Computer graphics, 18, 168
Connected component, 134
Connected set, 119, 134
Connectivity, 155–156
Convex hull, 149
Convexity, 119, 149
Convolution, 40, 64–65
  theorem, 42–43
Coordinate conversion, 151–152
Cross correlation, 40, 52–55
  normalized, 73
Cross-section, 123
Curvature, 31, 149, 164
Curve following, *see* Border following

D

Description
  of line drawings, 168–171
  of pictures, *see* Picture description
  of relationships among objects, 171–172
Diameter, 159
Diffraction, 62
  grating, 66
  sinusoidal, 62
Digital picture, 2
Digitization, 20
Directed part, 148
Directional differencing, 94–95, 100–101
Distance (function), 141–142, 159–160
  regular, 142